FIRESIDE

Cook with Me
SUGAR

FREE

Favorite Snacks, Sweets,
and Desserts for Children
and Grown-ups Too

SHARON M. DREGNE GERSTENZANG

Illustrations by Rhoda Watel

A FIRESIDE BOOK
Published by Simon & Schuster, Inc.
New York

DEDICATED
to the Almighty—
and to children everywhere

A Fireside Book
Published by Simon & Schuster, Inc.
Simon & Schuster Building
Rockefeller Center
1230 Avenue of the Americas
New York, New York 10020
FIRESIDE and colophon are registered trademarks of Simon & Schuster, Inc.
Designed by Irving Perkins Associates
Manufactured in the United States of America
Printed and bound by Fairfield Graphics
10 9 8 7 6 5 4 3
Library of Congress Cataloging in Publication Data
Gerstenzang, Sharon M. Dregne.
    Cook with me sugar free.

    "A Fireside book."
    Includes index.
    1. Sugar-free diet—Recipes.   2. Snack foods.
3. Desserts.   I. Title.
RM237.85.G47   1983   641.5'63   83-506
ISBN: 0-671-46472-8

Acknowledgments

I am deeply grateful to many people who have encouraged and helped me in my work on this cookbook.

First, I would like to express my appreciation to those who have worked directly with me on the project: Rhoda Watel, my artist, for her beautiful illustrations and her devotion to the project; Phyllis Bono, my typist, for her competent transcription and conscientious meeting of deadlines; Dixie Greer, R. D., M. E. D., nutritionist, for her invaluable consultation; and Angela Miller, my editor, for believing in the book, for supporting it, and for encouraging me to write about my ideas on nutrition.

Second, I want to thank family, friends, and acquaintances who have sampled these foods, and who have shared with me both their honest enthusiasm and their frank criticism: my husband, Alex, and our daughter, Jessica (you should only know the criticism of a one-and-a-half year old!); my parents, H. E. and Mary Dregne; my sisters, Nancy Dregne, Diane Dregne-Cabrero, and Arleen Ritter and her husband Mitch; Kevin, Cheryl, and Ann Rocco; Susan Murray; Jonathan and Toby Mardis Katz; Ellyn and Phil Polsky and family; Bonnie and Garry Vickar and family; Esther and Charles Abramson and family; Ruth and Ed Mihevc and family; Denise and Jerome Fondren; Carol and Don Berra and family and neighbors; Ilah and Gene Thompson; Denise and Jim Breeden and daughters; Stan and Ellen Levitz Jones; Shauna Reitz and family; Susan Reidhead and sons; Barb Weiman; Katie Danforth, Valerie Wooten, and the graduate students and staff of the Department of Psychology of the University of Missouri—St. Louis; the children and

5

adults of Tiffany Towne Court, especially Marilyn and Kareem Abdul-Haaq, and Char Lee; Lou MacFarland and the staff of the Diagnostic and Treatment Section and the typing pool of the St. Louis City Juvenile Court; the children and staff of the University of Missouri—St. Louis Child Development Center; the staff—especially Jim Wallhermfechtel—and patients of the Day Treatment Center; and the patients—especially Glenroy— and staff of 50N2 of the St. Louis V. A. Medical Center; Bob Schneider, Ken Bohm, and my fellow interns at the V. A. M. C.

Third, I would like to thank my family and friends who have neither sampled nor seen a recipe, yet were wholeheartedly optimistic and enthusiastic about the book from its inception: Sonja Eisenberg, Joni Preiser, Helen C. Grant, Barbara Weldon, and Roni Lett.

I want to express special gratitude to Barbara Reiss, senior editor of Bobbs-Merrill, Inc., and Rosalyn Baldalmanti, freelance cookbook editor, for their role in getting the cookbook to Fireside Press.

Finally, I want to mention my debt to several particularly salient sources that have contributed over the years to the development of the ideas which finally culminated in this cookbook: *Prevention Magazine; Feed Your Kids Right,* by Lendon Smith; *Let's Have Healthy Children,* by Adele Davis; *Diet for a Small Planet,* by Francis Moore Lappe; *Joy of Cooking,* by Rombauer and Becker; *The Good Goodies,* by Stan and Floss Dworkin; and *Jane Brody's Nutrition Book,* by Jane Brody, health editor for *The New York Times.*

Thank you everyone!

Sharon M. Dregne Gerstenzang

Introduction

My whole purpose in life seems to be to get the world to stop eating junk food. Now with Sharon's classic the world can eat what it perceives as junk and yet get good nutrition and some satisfaction of the sweet cravings.

The vast majority of my patients, and those who write to me, and those who call in on the radio shows tell me that they cannot resist sweets, but at the same time they want to be healthy and eat whole foods. This book has arrived at precisely the right time to catch all those who have this double need.

Sharon knows whereof she speaks. She admits to sugar addiction, and knows that even the most reluctant victims of sugar cravings will eventually find themselves back in the sugar bowl unless better alternatives are found. She suggests, too, that this problem can dispose susceptible individuals to yet other addictions . . . something I have seen in my own practice. I have one patient, for example, who begins to crave alcohol within one day of eating naked or impoverished sweets!

The author has observed that people who substitute sugar-free sweets from her recipes for sugary foods seem to lose their cravings for sugar. When they do try sugary, refined food again, they tend to find the food either a) too sweet b) unsatisfying or c) nauseating (apparently a reaction to the alkalinity of refined sugar).

Sharon goes on to point out that although superior to sugar and honey, even dried fruits and juice concentrates should not be constantly consumed. So, watch it! Bear in mind, as she advises, that this book is intended as a tool, enabling cooks to compete with junk food while edging more toward the goal of keeping refined foods out of their diets and those of their families. Danger does still lurk in these desserts if you overuse them because, although the desserts are good for you, fresh whole fruits are better. But if you heed Sharon's warning—to nibble good food every three or so hours, and cut down gradually on the sweeteners once you are accustomed to the sugar-free sweets—then you can enjoy a full spectrum of sweet things without gaining too much weight or feeling guilty because you are enjoying your food.

Lendon H. Smith, M.D.

Preface

More and more, people seem to be trying to reduce the amount of sugar in their diets. I have been working on it for years: battling my own sweet tooth and the presence of refined sugar in foods everywhere, worrying about how I was going to keep my own children from falling prey to the lure of such nonnutritious treats. This cookbook represents the culmination, thus far, of my efforts to make healthy substitutes for the refined-sugar-containing goodies I grew up knowing and loving.

In this cookbook, "sugar" is used to refer to any nutritionally impoverished sweetener, including honey (see Table 1 and Glossary). Instead of sugar, the major sweeteners used are higher-nutrient juice concentrates and dried fruit. Whole-grain flours and soy and nonfat dry-milk powders are used in many recipes in order to optimize the protein quality, as well as the nutrient and fiber content of the snacks and desserts. In creating these recipes, I have worked to *duplicate as closely as possible the nation's favorite sweets.* The foods have met with widespread approval and enthusiasm from children and adults of all ages. Also, in creating the recipes, I have streamlined them to be as easy as possible to follow in order that busy family members may have time to fit their preparations into packed schedules.

But I have taken the concepts only so far: I believe that there is room for the application of sugar-free cooking and baking to go much further. So, in order that you can continue to experiment, and progress beyond the limits of this book, I have laid out in detail the methods by which you, too, can create your own refined-sugarless recipes. I hope that you, and others, will take these ideas, expand them, improve on them, and spread them across the country. Good luck, fellow cooks!

Sharon M. Dregne Gerstenzang

Table 1. Nutritional Values Per 1 Cup of Sweetener

Sweetener	Calories	Calcium (in milligrams)	Phosphorus (in milligrams)	Iron (in milligrams)	Potassium (in milligrams)	Vitamin A (in International Units)	Thiamine (in milligrams)	Riboflavin (in milligrams)	Niacin (in milligrams)	Vitamin C (in milligrams)
white sugar	770	0	0	.8	24	0	0	0	0	0
honey	1,040	16	16	.1	11	0	0	.16	1.6	0
brown sugar	820	187	42	7.5	757	0	.02	.07	.4	0
blackstrap* molasses	720	2,192	272	51.2	9,360	0	.32	.64	6.4	0
unsweetened apple-juice concentrate	480	60	88	6.0	1,000	0	.08	.20	.8	8
unsweetened orange-juice concentrate	480	100	168	1.2	2,000	2,160	.91	.15	3.7	480
unsweetened pineapple-juice concentrate	560	162	92	3.2	1,392	520	.52	.20	2.0	320
dates, chopped (24 medium)	490	105	112	5.3	1,153	90	.16	.18	3.9	0
raisins	420	90	146	5.1	1,106	30	.16	.12	.7	1
prunes	255	51	79	3.8	695	1,590	.07	.15	1.5	2.0

*The figures for molasses are impressively high; the trouble with molasses is that it is very strongly flavored, and chemically laden from the refinement process for white sugar.

Table of Contents

RECIPES

CHAPTER **1**

Problems of the American Diet

Although Americans live longer than they did at the turn of the century, the increased longevity is due almost exclusively to the eradication and control of infectious diseases through such techniques as improved sanitation, antibiotics, and immunizations. But because of our diets, we are not living nearly as long as we might. Also, since the turn of the century, there have been dramatic rises in diet-related diseases, including heart disease, stroke, diabetes, cancer, and hypertension. Major critical contributors to this sorry state of nutrition are too much sugar in our diets, far too much fat (especially of the saturated variety), and too few unrefined complex carbohydrates.

TROUBLES WITH SUGAR

There is considerable debate over precisely what role sugar has in our problems. Certainly it is a major contributor to the rampant problem of obesity, which in turn predisposes us to many diseases and generally poor health. It has also been cited as a specific precipitating factor in diseases that run the gamut from tooth decay and acne to diabetes and irritable bowel syndrome. Evidence exists that sugar may also contribute to the behavioral problems of hyperactivity and aggressiveness in children and irritability and depression in adults. But whatever the specifics, simple common sense suggests that sugar would certainly undermine anyone's overall health if used in any but very small quantities. It is extremely high in calories per unit of volume, yet virtually devoid of essential nutrients, enzymes, and fiber

(see Table 1, p. 10). To the extent that it replaces more nutri-ent-rich foods, our health is bound to suffer.

And replace nutrient-rich foods it has. Current per capita consumption of sugar is estimated at 140 pounds per person per year—and is continuing to rise. The critical questions to be asked are: "Why is the consumption of sugar so very high? Why isn't it consumed in moderation?" It appears that with sugar, many of us go to excess. Our overindulgence in refined-sugar sweets resembles the pattern of dependence on sugar's near relative, alcohol: we have "binges" and "cravings" and contin-ue to eat sweets even when we feel full. Certainly these are hall-marks of an addictive cycle involving sugar. But why is this so? How does this happen?

WHY CHILDREN (AND ADULTS) LOVE SWEETS

In answering the question of "Why do we overeat sugar?" we must first recognize that to like sweet tastes is biologically natu-ral. We are geared to enjoy sweet tastes because the foods we need for survival (from the breast milk needed by infants, to the grains, vegetables, and fruits we eat as adults) are at their most edible when also at their sweetest. This ordinarily adap-tive orientation toward sweet foods extends even to the realm of vision. Look at the fruit and vegetable sections of your supermarket—especially in summertime. The array of color is vibrant—and mouth-watering.

And then look at where else we have sweet tastes and eye-catching colors: in candies, cookies, cakes, and pastries. But this time the vibrant colors are artificial, and the sweetness they herald is a sweetness far removed from vital nutrients and fiber.

WHY WE OVEREAT SWEETS: OVERRIDING NATURAL SATIETY INDICATORS

But natural inclination is not the whole answer. We simply don't see people "binging" on fresh fruit and vegetables and whole-grain bread the way we do on refined-sugar-containing sweets. What is the difference?

I believe that one major problem is that highly sweetened (as well as highly salted) foods actually stimulate overeating. They do this in part by overriding our natural "Okay, I'm satisfied" (i.e., satiety) indicators.

The first major indicator of satiety is salivation. If you are eating a nonrefined-sugar-containing and nonsalted food, you will notice that when you have had a certain amount, the food will start to taste differently—and you will salivate less. Conversely, you have probably noticed that when you are very hungry, you salivate a great deal. Unfortunately, highly sugared and highly salted foods stimulate intense salivation even when one is no longer hungry. Two common statements that reflect

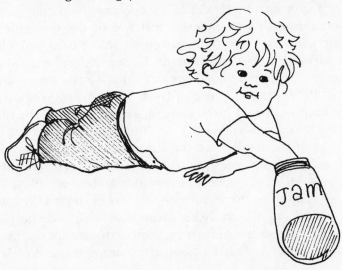

this experience are "I can always find room for dessert" and "Once I get started, I can eat a whole bag of potato chips."

The second major indicator of satiety is stomach fullness. While our stomachs only hold so much by volume, our capacity for calories varies widely according to how high in calories a food is for a given volume. White-sugar foods are extraordinarily high in calories per unit volume not only by virtue of the sugar they contain, but also because they are often also very high in fat content, and are generally made with white rather than with whole-grain flour. As a result, it requires quite a few calories before our tummies begin to feel well-filled. . . .

DISRUPTION OF NORMAL METABOLISM

Another factor in the tendency to become "addicted" to or binge on refined-sugar sweets is related to the quantities in which we eat them, and their extremely low nutritional value. Simple carbohydrates (white sugar, honey, natural fruit sugar, milk sugar) are metabolized very rapidly. Consuming simple sugars in the form of a piece of fresh fruit sets off a relatively low rise in blood-sugar level, though, as compared to the much more highly sugared candy bar or doughnut. This means that in the case of the fresh fruit, the simple carbohydrate gives us energy, and the body does not have to secrete large amounts of insulin in order to use up any excess. But in the case of the candy bar or doughnut, there is a gross excess of sugar very quickly, and the pancreas literally goes into overdrive in response. It secretes large amounts of insulin in order to use up the excess sugar. The result is that an hour after eating a piece of fruit, you may be a little hungry; but an hour after the candy bar or doughnut, you are likely to feel drained, because the blood sugar will have fallen lower than it was before you ate due to the overabundance of insulin in your system. If we have become accustomed to eating refined-sugar sweets, we will respond to this feeling of hunger by repeating the cycle all over again.

In addition to blood-sugar levels, I suspect that there are other factors at work. I have no hard proof of this, but it seems to me and to others with whom I have spoken that our bodies signal hunger not only when there is a need for the basic elements of carbohydrates and protein—for energy and tissue-building, respectively—but also when there is a need for the catalysts of metabolism: vitamins, minerals, and enzymes. Not only do sugar and honey not supply these essential catalysts— but they also actually consume nutrients from other foods you have eaten. For example, in order to utilize glucose, the body requires comparatively large amounts of B vitamins. When you eat a refined-sugar and white-flour product, you are consuming many nutrient-empty calories (sugar) along with many relatively low-fiber and nutrient-poor calories (white flour). So, you end up with a double nutritional debt. Those of us habituated to such foods have no basis for comparison, so we fail to recognize that we are actually feeling discomfort due to the foods we have eaten. We then eat still more of the impoverished foods in

our vain and unconscious efforts to achieve a feeling of well-being. I suspect that this underlying imbalance due to the foods we eat may make us easy prey, too, for a whole spectrum of other "addicting substances" that plague our society—such as salt, caffeine, nicotine, alcohol, amphetamines, barbiturates, cocaine, and heroin. Once out of touch with our bodies, it is easier to be "hooked" by other chemicals which artificially counterbalance the imbalances.

THE CARBOHYDRATE MYTH

We often hear "carbohydrates" being maligned for their fattening qualities, and talked about as if they are of little value in ordinary diet. Nothing could be further from the truth. In fact, they are our primary source of energy.

Yet, there is an element of truth in that statement as far as *simple* carbohydrates are concerned. Simple carbohydrates are abundant in fruit—and overabundant in refined sugar- and honey-containing desserts. We do indeed, by virtue of man-made products, have far, far too much nutrient-poor simple carbohydrates in our diets.

But complex carbohydrates are *essential* to the human diet. Unlike simple carbohydrates, they are accompanied in nature by a whole complement of B vitamins to aid in their metabolism. Far from being villains, unrefined complex-carbohydrate foods offer the best of all possible worlds in terms of both weight control and general well-being. Complex carbohydrates are abundant in starchy foods: bread, rice, pasta, peas, beans,

rice, corn, potatoes. They are low in calories per unit volume (and so give a satisfying feeling of stomach fullness for relatively few calories) and extraordinarily high in dietary fiber and the nutrients required for metabolization of carbohydrates. They go into the human bloodstream at an optimum rate—neither as slowly as fats, nor as quickly as simple carbohydrates. Insulin levels therefore stay best modulated with complex carbohydrates.

The implication of nutritional data surrounding complex carbohydrates is that they should comprise 60 percent to 80 percent of the total carbohydrates that we eat, and 40 percent to 60 per cent of the total calories of our diets. This means that simple carbohydrates and animal protein should assume a much smaller place than they currently have in the average American diet.

FATS: TOO MANY, TOO SATURATED

All we really need in order to satisfy nutritional requirements is about one tablespoonful of unsaturated fat a day. We have no need whatsoever for saturated fats. Yet Americans get far, far too much fat, primarily from high-saturated-fat animal proteins, partially-saturated-fat-laden sweets, including pies, doughnuts, and cookies, and deep-fried favorites such as French fries.

The more saturated a fat is, the more solid it is at room temperature. Beef, pork, chicken fat, vegetable shortening, and butter are all very highly saturated fats. Vegetable oils and fish oils are unsaturated (liquid at room temperature). Margarine and eggs both contain a large proportion of saturated fats. And any time something is deep-fried, even if in vegetable oil, part of the fat becomes saturated.

Ideally, at least two-thirds of the fats we consume should be unsaturated. If this balance is reached, then unsaturated fats can offset the saturated fat impact on the body. In order to accomplish this and at the same time have a reasonably low fat content in the overall diet, national consumption of meat, poultry, of high-fat dairy products such as butter and cheese and deep-fried foods would have to decline sharply. The decline in foods high in protein and fat would not, incidentally, have to be offset by an equal increase in consumption of high protein, low-fat foods because adult Americans already consume more than twice as much protein as they need. This excess protein is not only not useful for food energy, it also puts extra stress on the kidneys which have to break it down and excrete it.

CULTURE: BAD HABITS ON A GRAND SCALE— WITH SUGAR CENTER-STAGE

From the beginning of life, food and nuturance are paired: the infant is held and cuddled while s/he is nursed or bottle-fed. As time goes on, the child gradually should learn that caring is different from eating or giving food. But there are factors that continue to operate against learning that important fact, playing instead into the illusion that food and caring must go hand in hand. Often food—especially sweet food—is used as a reward, as a consolation, as an expression of camaraderie. No wonder that many of us eat cookies or gorge on cake when sad or lonely instead of seeking only a good listener and, perhaps, a loving hug. Examples of our confusion of food with praise and love are "If you're a good boy (girl) you can have dessert"; "I just broke up with my boyfriend, too—let's go console ourselves on a banana split"; "Why are you crying? Are you hungry? Do you want something to eat?" (this to the preverbal toddler); "You won! Let's celebrate! The ice cream is on me for the whole team!"

Another major adverse influence is advertising. From TV ads to vending machines, magazines to billboards, we are inces-

santly inundated with convincing presentations of candy bars, soft drinks, presweetened cereals, succulent meat, and flavorful cheeses—while the growers of fruits, vegetables, and grains are left hard put to compete for our attention. Vending machines lie in wait for hungry passersby who, unarmed by their own nutritious snacks, fall easy prey to the temptations of very sugary and very salty foods. A visit to the movies brings us immediately in view of a whole array of similarly nonnutritive but very tasty foods.

Besides all the obvious sources of sugar, much of it is hidden in everything from soups to crackers, salad dressings to whipping cream. Manufacturers are all too well aware of the added taste appeal of that bit (or lot) of sugar. And when you go through a normal day—with the heavy association of refined-sugar sweets with such common events as preschoolers' snack times, lunch out with friends, or a birthday party at the office— you might well despair of ever breaking the cycle of overeating sugar. It's almost like the alcoholic who has to try to eschew liquor while spending all of his or her time in a bar. Difficult, to say the least. So, what can we do?

CHAPTER **2**

Sugar-Free the Family

Cutting down on sugar, because of those factors mentioned in the previous chapter, can be one of the hardest changes to make in our diets. I would like to suggest three major means of freeing ourselves from the lure of refined-sugar-containing foods:

1. Substitute unrefined foods for refined ones, and relatively low-calorie foods for those high in fat;
2. Provide an adequate daily supply of snacks and minimeals to satisfy each person's hunger throughout the day in order that you and they will not fall prey to all-too-available refined sweets;
3. Prepare sweets at home which will approximate the taste and texture of refined-sugar sweets but have much better nutritive value, and which are relatively easy to prepare.

TRADING IN SUGAR AND HONEY

Obviously, the easiest way to accustom children to unrefined foods is to start them at home, very young. But most of us have older children who have already picked up bad food habits. Getting them to participate willingly in an effort to oust sugar and honey and white flour may require a sustained spirit of cooperative enterprise.

The approach I would like to suggest is a relaxed and interested one in which everyone learns to share in the responsibility for creating and eating nutritious and delicious foods.

Explain your interest in finding treats that taste delicious (like the white sugar ones) and are also good to one's tummy and body (unlike the white sugar and white flour ones). Enlist your children's aid as much as possible in the food preparation, especially of the new sweets, even though it will make things slower at first. For in the long run, the shared responsibility will make the experimentation and new foods more of a joy for everyone. Certainly you can expect rejections—but don't despair, eventually change does take place. You can also expect them to like—and, for a while, prefer—sugary sweets available outside the home. After all, everyone else has them, and they're associated with good times. But if you continue the experimentation and cooperation, gently trying to accommodate their tastes while also trying to incorporate your food values, you will eventually get good results.

In encouraging change, I advise against prohibiting sugar-containing foods when the child is offered them outside the home. For one thing, forbidden sweets are likely to take on a desirability far exceeding their original attractiveness. For another, I believe that the gestures of giving and receiving often have an importance that outweighs the food value, especially among younger children. Instead, I would suggest setting a good example. For instance, you might let your young child take a cookie, but decline to take one yourself, explaining "I would rather eat something good for me, even though that does taste good." Or when your older child offers you a sugary sweet, accept a small taste, and express appreciation for the sweetness and the gesture, but decline to eat any more, "Because I know that I just won't feel as good as I'd like to afterward if I eat much more."

Remember, too, that among more sugar-and-white-flour-habituated family members, resistance to change may be high. In this case, it may be helpful to maintain a significant proportion of white flour in your recipes, and/or to add some sugar in order to accommodate to their tastes. If you do use sugar, I recommend brown sugar as the least of the evils, with a taste close enough to that of white sugar (see Table 1). Over time, the proportion of sugar or white flour may be reduced and, finally, eliminated, if that is your goal.

THE SUGAR-FREE LUNCHBOX

I agree with Lendon Smith, M.D., who contends that people should eat every three or so hours in order to keep blood sugar and, hence, energy levels optimal. I suspect that failure to fol-

low such a regimen with nutritious foods is yet another reason why we overeat sweets. Five to six hours between meals frequently leads to ravenous appetites that can create "eyes bigger than our stomachs" and the motive to stuff ourselves. As one friend said, "It's almost as if I keep on eating just remembering how hungry I was."

The implication of this is that as you prepare your own or your spouse's or your child's food for the next day, you should keep in mind midmorning and midafternoon snacks as well as lunch. As an example of this type of eating, consider dividing the sandwich and the banana in half, with half of each eaten midmorning, and the remainder at noon. Then, in the afternoon, one could have crackers with milk, rice with nuts, or leftover pasta, or a sugar-free, unfrosted cake or muffin. Keep in mind that the starches (even if refined) should figure first, with cheese, meat, egg, etc., serving to round out the protein content required rather than as the central caloric focus of the meal. For older children and adults, I recommend providing also an abundance of their favorite raw vegetables such as carrots, green beans, mushrooms, cucumbers, bell peppers, yellow squash or zucchini slices, celery, radishes, and tomatoes. These may be offered to younger children, too, but generally toddlers and young preschoolers aren't very good at eating foods with such coarse or dry textures, although they will enjoy nibbling at them.

When everyone is home, both breakfast and dinner should be relatively light—no one meal should be much larger than a moderate snack. Remember, too, that small children require especially small portions. For example, it is easy for an adult to think that dinner of one tablespoonful of egg and two to three tablespoonfuls each of peas and rice is awfully scanty. But for a toddler, it may be practically perfect. You might want to try also a high-protein bedtime snack for everyone: Lendon Smith recommends this as one way of achieving more congenial and energetic risings the next morning.

THE TRANSITION TO SUGAR FREEDOM

Even when you have a fully nutritious diet, replete with fresh fruit and vegetables, you are likely to want to have some of your favorite sweets. Sentimentality, feeling left out of the mainstream, a whim for self-indulgence, or simple habit are all moti-

vators with which we have to reckon. Moreover, these reasons assume enormous importance in the world of children, where what the other child has to eat can be the most fascinating item of the lunch hour. So, once you've found the treats he or she enjoys, it pays to send your child forth armed with sweetly delicious foods that can compete with the other children's Twinkies and Ding-Dongs. I also recommend sending no-sugar sweets periodically in large supply in order that your child can share liberally with other children.

One problem that may arise, particularly early in the transition period, is that the more sugar-jaded anyone's palate, the less sweet the desserts and snacks in this cookbook may taste (although some will please even the greatest sugar aficionados). But you have only to stay away from sugar for a day or two to find your tastes beginning to change. And the more you eschew sugar, the more you will enjoy these sugar-free desserts. As an example of this effect, taste a glass of orange juice after eating some presweetened cereal. Then, another day, taste the same brand of orange juice with an unsweetened breakfast of eggs and toast. Note how much sweeter the orange juice tastes on the egg day, and how much more acidic it tastes on the sugary cereal day.

As you find sweets that appeal to you and your family, I recommend making them up (particularly cookies) in large quantities and freezing them, in order to keep work to a minimum. The recipes in this cookbook are streamlined to be as quick and easy to follow as possible. Even most cake recipes are very speedy. Cookie doughs can be made and then frozen or chilled, making it possible to prepare them in stages. Chopping of nuts and measuring of dry ingredients can be done in the morning; mixing and baking can be done later.

AND REMEMBER ... A GOAL

Once the transition has been made from sugar-containing foods, I recommend trying to reduce the proportion of juice concentrates and dried fruits used in the recipes of this book. I also recommend that the sweets be kept secondary to fresh fruit, as the latter is the very best source of nutrition. Dried fruits, incidentally, are very concentrated, and probably not even as desirable as the baked sweets of this cookbook. Sweetness reductions are particularly appropriate in such items as puddings, popsicles, and beverages. Reduction of sweetener proportions may be less successful in cookies and cakes where just the sight of food may be associated with expectancy of a very high sweetness level. The goal, after all, is better nutrition and adequate competition with a sugary world while trying to keep the simple carbohydrates in our diets at a modest level.

3

Converting Your Own Recipes to Sugar Free

"Whatever your action,
Food or worship;
Whatever the gift
That you give to another;
Whatever you vow to the work of the spirit . . .
Lay these also
As offerings before me."
—Bhagavad Gita

It seems to me that every one of the principles I have used in creating sugar-free recipes is known to all of us at some level. For example, that milk is a sweetener: How many of us have tasted the sweetness of a cold glass of milk, although we may not have put it into those words? Or that toasting grains increases their sweetness: Why do you think toast at breakfast is so popular in our culture? And haven't we all noticed, somehow, that date-nut and raisin breads seem especially sweet compared to other sweet breads—and oatmeal-raisin cookies especially mouth-watering compared to peanut-butter or even, for some of us, chocolate-chip cookies? So, although many of the following principles and techniques may appear new to you, perhaps even forbidding at first, they may soon seem very familiar. . . .

Table 2.　Combinations and Ratios of Sweeteners to Other
Ingredients

Ingredient Amount	Recommended Sweetener(s)	Type of Recipe	Recommended Amount of Sweetener
whole-grain flour, 1 cup	dates; apple-juice and pineapple-juice concentrates	cakes	Substitute 1½ cups date flour, plus 0–4 T juice concentrate
		cookies	Substitute 1½ cups date flour, plus 0–8 T thickened juice concentrate or dried fruit purée
		muffins, breads, pancakes	¼–½ cup of juice concentrate or dried-fruit purée
tropical fruit, 1 cup			2–4 T
—bananas	apple-juice concentrate	(any)	
—pineapple	pineapple-juice and apple-juice concentrates; golden raisins	(any)	
northern and semitropical fruit, 1 cup		custards, puddings, frozen desserts, beverages, sauces, fillings	¼ cup + 1 T
—apples	apple-juice concentrate; dates; raisins		
—apricots, peaches	apple-juice concentrate plus pineapple concentrate; golden raisins	jams, jellies, butters	⅓–½ cup
—blueberries, cherries, blackberries	pear-grape concentrate; dates		
—oranges,	apple-juice		

Table 2. Continued

Ingredient Amount	Recommended Sweetener(s)	Type of Recipe	Recommended Amount of Sweetener
rasp-berries, straw-berries	concentrate plus orange-juice concentrate; golden raisins		
milk or cream, 1 cup	dates or raisins; pear-grape or apple-juice concentrate	puddings, custards, beverages, frozen desserts	¼ cup
yogurt or buttermilk	juice concentrates	(any)	⅓–½ cup
cream cheese, 8 oz.	dates; raisins	cheesecakes, frostings	⅓–⅔ cup
baking chocolate, 1 oz., or cocoa, 3 T	pear-grape concentrate; dates	(any)	½–¾ cup
carob powder, 1 cup	bananas; evaporated milk; raisins; prunes; prune juice	(any)	1 cup 1¼ cup ¼ cup 1 cup

Note: All recipes made with the above sweeteners, and without sugar or honey, should be refrigerated if not eaten within a day or two. The reason for this is that sugar is a preservative, and sugar-free baking is therefore baking entirely without any preservative.

SWEETENING PRINCIPLES

There are six major sources of sweetness which are helpful to consider in sugar-free cooking: 1. unsweetened fruit-juice concentrates; 2. dried fruit; 3. fresh and frozen fruits; 4. milk; 5. fats; 6. whole grains.

1. Unsweetened Fruit-Juice Concentrates

For both unsweetened juice concentrates and dried fruit, 1½ to 1¾ cup of the sweetener is roughly equivalent in sweetening power to 1 cup of sugar. However, many dessert recipes are oversugared, so you should also refer to Table 2 when trying to determine how much sweetener to use instead of sugar or honey. When you use juice concentrates, they have several traits that should be kept in mind for successful cooking:

a. Juices (and dried fruits) cannot melt and recrystallize like sugar, therefore cookies and candies will always be relatively soft as compared to sugar-based cooking; eggs are relied upon for the cohesiveness of the finished product;

b. Juices (and dried fruits) can curdle hot milk; to prevent this, puddings must be made by first thickening the milk with cornstarch, and then adding a beaten-together combination of juice and egg; curdling is not a problem in baking (as for custards) because of the combination of low temperature with the presence of eggs beaten into the liquid;

c. Juices activate baking soda, so cakes involving juice concentrates do not require either a sour milk or baking powder (see baking soda and baking powder in Glossary);

d. Juices burn at lower temperatures than sugar, so cookies must not be baked at high oven temperatures.

The unsweetened juice concentrates that we have readily available in our supermarkets, and that are particularly useful in sugar-free cooking, are apple-juice concentrate, pineapple-juice concentrate, pear-grape concentrate, and orange-juice concentrate. *Apple-juice concentrate* is used most often in these sugar-free recipes because it comes in large cans, is less expensive than pineapple-juice concentrate, and has a flavor which can be reasonably well obscured by flavor extracts (e.g., vanilla extract, almond extract). Depending upon your palate, *pineapple-juice concentrate* may make desserts taste sweeter for you than apple-juice concentrate, and it may be substituted wherever apple-juice concentrate is called for. Also, the sweetness of pineapple-juice concentrate seems to be enhanced when it is combined with apple-juice concentrate in a 2:1 ratio. *Pear-grape concentrate* is used primarily in conjunction with chocolate because it seems to complement the chocolate flavor better than apple-juice concentrate. However, either apple-juice concentrate or pineapple-juice concentrate, or a combination of the two, may be substituted for the pear-grape concentrate with relatively good results. *Orange-juice concentrate* has the tartest overtones of any of the juice concentrates, so it is almost always used in a 2:1 ratio with apple-juice concentrate. Its tartness has

an effect similar to that obtained by lemon juice in sugar-based cooking.

The ways juice concentrates may be used are as follows:

a. Thawed, substituted directly for the milk, water, or oil called for in a recipe; if substituted for oil, much smaller to equal volumes of butter or margarine may be used in order to compensate for the effect of the fat*;

b. Thickened with 2 tablespoons cornstarch or arrowroot powder (see Glossary) per cup, and substituted for the honey called for in a recipe;

c. Combined with fresh fruit or vegetables and a small amount of oil, butter, or margarine (to prevent burning and boiling over) and boiled vigorously for about 4 minutes uncovered or 7 minutes covered (this may vary with altitude) in order to get rid of extra moisture before inclusion in the recipe.

2. Dried Fruit

The sweetness hierarchy for dried fruit, from sweetest to least sweet, is approximately as follows: dates, dark raisins, golden raisins, currants, black mission figs, dried banana, dried pineapple, Turkish figs, prunes, apricots, peaches, pears, and apples. Unfortunately, some dried fruits—especially date pieces and pineapple—are frequently pre-dusted with sugar (usually fructose). So, purists, beware! In this cookbook, mainly dates

**Note:* The volume of fat used in this cookbook's cake and cookie recipes is considerably less than most recipes call for.

and raisins are called for because of both their sweetness and their ready availability. Dried fruits may be incorporated into sugar-free cooking in the following ways:

a. Ground in a blender or food processor with whole-wheat flour and some soy powder to make a fruity flour similar in consistency to cornmeal (see Date Flour under Basic Sweeteners); such flours may be substituted for white or whole-wheat flour in the ratio of 1½ cups of fruit flour per cup of regular flour;

b. Soaked overnight or for 24 hours in water, milk, or cream in order to yield a sweet and relatively nonfruity-tasting liquid (see Raisin Milk under Basic Sweeteners);

c. Combined with water and/or juice or juice concentrates and boiled vigorously, covered, for 5 minutes, and then puréed in a blender or food processor, or strained or mashed by hand, in order to yield a jamlike sweetener (see Prune Purée under Basic Sweeteners).

The last method was used in more of my preliminary recipes but later phased out because other methods involved fewer steps. However, dried fruit purées, as well as the left-over fruit from fruit soaks, may be kept on hand under refrigeration and used as quick and ready sweetening, especially for pancakes and cookies. Also, this is still the main method used in making sugar-free candies and cream-cheese cheesecakes.

3. Fresh and Frozen Fruits

Puréed thawed fruit, puréed fresh fruit cooked with some water, and regular (not concentrated) canned fruit juices may all be substituted for milk, water, or oil called for in a recipe (see previous section: Unsweetened Fruit-Juice Concentrates). This method is particularly useful in preparing puddings, custards, frozen desserts, and beverages.

Bananas (see Glossary) and pineapple, when at their optimum ripeness, are the two sweetest of commonly available fruits. They require somewhat less sweetening per unit volume than do other fruits and regular fruit juices (see Table 2). Frozen fruits and regular canned juices are often actually sweeter than their fresh counterparts available in supermarkets because the fruit used in making them has been picked at maturation,

when fully sweet and ripe, rather than picked green or slightly underripe in order to accommodate for shipping. Fresh or thawed fruit or the canned juice of the fruit all require approximately the same amount of the concentrated fruit sweeteners in order to achieve dessertlike sweetness.

4. Milk

Milk—whether whole (3%), part skim, or skim—requires no more sweetener than the same amount of fresh fruit (see Table 2). This is because of the high concentrate of lactose found in cow's milk. To further enhance sweetness, evaporated milk (either skim or whole—both have more than double the concentration of lactose found in regular milk) or nonfat dry milk may be used for extra sweetening. The evaporated milk may be substituted directly for part of the regular milk; the nonfat dry milk may be used in combination with water, and may be used in a larger volume than would ordinarily be required for reconstituting milk. For example, in a pudding or custard, the volume of fruit plus fruit juice may equal 1 cup. That would indicate a need for $\frac{1}{4}$ cup of noninstant or 5 tablespoons of instant nonfat dry milk to compensate for the volume of regular milk being replaced by the fruit plus juice. Moreover, you may add several

extra tablespoonfuls to add to the sweetness. Similarly, nonfat dry milk may be added to cookies and cakes. In cookies, there is no need to add extra liquid, even for volumes of nonfat dry milk up to one-half the volume of flour used in the recipe. However, in cakes you should add 1 tablespoon of water or juice or regular milk per every $\frac{1}{4}$ cup noninstant nonfat dry milk used. Then repeat blending process.

5. Fats

Cream and butter enhance sweetness better than margarine, oils, or vegetable shortening. However, all fats, especially roasted nuts, can enhance the experience of sweetness to a greater or lesser degree (this is partly why we tend to butter our bread and toast). Examples of this effect are the seemingly high sweetness level of doughnuts and fritters despite the low proportion of dried fruit or unsweetened fruit-juice concentrate used in their preparation. Another example is the Carob Butter Cookies, in which only carob flour (actually a fruit, not a grain; see Glossary), nuts, and butter are used.

6. Whole Grains

Whole grains are naturally sweet, and they are at their sweetest when used immediately after grinding (see grains in Glossary). Within 18 hours after grinding, oxidation progresses to a degree that results in slightly sour flour. For this reason it is often advised that whole-grain flours be stored in the refrigerator. But since most commercially available flour is nonrefrigerated, shelf-stored, often for months at a time, this measure is not particularly useful. To offset the oxidation effect, you may want to try pan-roasting your whole-grain flour before use. In general, roasting enhances sweetness, whether in grain or in nuts (see Pan-Roasted Flour under Basic Sweeteners, and Roasted Nuts and Seeds under Miscellaneous Mixables).

BASIC SWEETENERS

1. Date Flour

Place in a blender in the following order
   ¾ cup whole-wheat flour   **2 T soy powder**
   ¾ cup date pieces (16
      medium dates)

Blend at top speed for about 1 minute. After starting blender, remove lid and gently stir the surface of the mixture, staying well away from the blender blades, while the blender is going. If necessary, stop blender and turn the mixture, using a knife or spatula in order to get the packed-down portion out of the bottom of the blender; then blend again. The finished product should be the color of light brown sugar and the consistency of cornmeal. Yields about 1½ cups date flour.

Variation: Other dried fruits, especially dark raisins, may be substituted for the dates.

Notes: 1. One pound of dates contains about 4 cups of dates (96 to 100 dates).
   2. Date pieces in bulk are usually cheaper than whole dates.
   3. For efficiency, I recommend using two measuring cups in

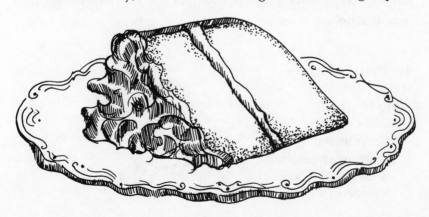

order that you may measure your next portions of flour, dates, and soy while the blender is still going.

4. I prefer to make up my date flour about two quarts or more at a time; it stores as well as regular flour, without refrigeration.

5. I encountered too-moist dates only once—in a holiday gift pack—but never from Del Monte, Sun Giant, etc. However, if you do happen to use dates that are too moist, the date flour will become very lumpy and hard to handle in the blender. If this happens, dry the mixture out on a cookie sheet at about 150° F in the oven for 2 hours.

2. Date Meal

During Passover, the same principles of sweetening can be applied. Crush and grind in a blender until fine-crumb consistency
   2 whole-wheat matzoth
Add:
   14 whole dates
Blend as for date flour.

3. Pan-Roasted Flour

Preheat a nonstick skillet (at least 9 inches in diameter) over medium-high heat. Pack
   2 cups whole grain flour
      and/or soy powder
evenly over the bottom of the skillet. Stir at 30- to 60-second intervals, repacking flour after each stirring. Cool to room temperature before using.

4. Prune Purée

Bring to a boil
   2 cups prunes
   ⅔ cup water
   ⅓ cup unsweetened
      pineapple-juice
      concentrate

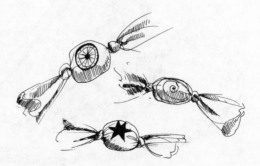

Cover. Reduce heat to medium-high. Boil for 5 minutes. Purée. Must be stored in refrigerator if not used in 2 to 3 days

Variations: 1. Substitute apple-juice concentrate for pineapple-juice concentrate.

2. Substitute raisins for prunes.

3. Substitute dates for prunes, and water for part or all of the unsweetened juice concentrate.

5. Raisin Milk

Soak for 24 hours, stirring once after about 12 hours
   ¼ cup raisins, chopped   1 cup milk
      for best effect

Use either the liquid alone, straining the raisins to get as much of the moisture out as possible, or use the liquid plus the raisins.

Variations: 1. Substitute dates for raisins.

2. Substitute water (for raisin "juice") or Half-and-Half or whipping cream for part or all of milk.

Note: Soaking overnight is also adequate, and results in a very sweet milk to use on cereal the next morning.

6. Unsweetened Fruit-Juice Concentrates

The latest full range of unsweetened juice concentrates that I have seen on the market includes apple juice, apple cider, pear-grape, pineapple, orange-pineapple and grapefruit. Juice concentrates can also be made at home. Bring to a boil in a large nonstick skillet
   1 quart juice
   1 tsp. oil
Let boil as vigorously as possible without excessive foaming for about 25 minutes.* The higher the altitude, the less moisture will evaporate in that length of time. Resulting liquid should be about 1 cup in volume.

*Variable according to altitude.

CHAPTER 4

Special Diet Considerations

DIABETES AND HYPOGLYCEMIA

In diabetes, especially, and, to a lesser degree, in hypoglycemia, it is critical to moderate the intake of foods that enter into the bloodstream either very rapidly (simple carbohydrates) or very slowly (fats). Therefore, even more than is true for the rest of us, diabetics and hypoglycemics should put their emphasis on consumption of starches and vegetable protein (complex carbohydrates) and, secondarily, on consumption of low-fat animal protein.

In this book, most—but not all—of the serving sizes in the recipes are appropriate for diabetics. The diabetic's serving should contain no more than two portions of a fruit (2 fruit) and no more than three to four portions of fat (3–4 fat). If a serving contains more than that of either fruit or fat, it is not appropriate for the diabetic to eat all in one sitting. In that case, you should either avoid the recipe altogether, or you should cut the serving size down in order to bring the number of fruit and fat portions within the proper limit allowed by your meal plan. For example, Apple Dumplings are too high in both fruit and fat for a diabetic (4 fruit, 6 fat). If you nevertheless want to eat some apple dumpling, eat just half a serving (2 fruit, 3 fat). Other examples are: 1. The serving sizes for fruit pies: fruit portions are too high for diabetics when the pie is cut into 8 pieces, but are within reasonable limits if the pie is cut into 10 even sections; 2. the serving sizes for some cream-

Table 3. Food Group Sources by Composition

Food Group	Calories in 1 portion	Carbohydrate (in grams)	Protein (in grams)	Fat (in grams)
Bread	70	15	2	0
Fat	45	0	0	5
Fruit	40	10	0	0
Meat (lean)*	55	0	7	3
Milk (skim)*	80	12	8	0
Vegetable	25	5	2	0

*All serving values in this cookbook are calculated assuming the use of skim milk in the recipe, and are based on the low-fat meat and low-fat milk portion figures.

cheese-based cheesecakes: fat portions are too high for diabetics, but are within reasonable limits if you take half servings (very small indeed); 3. the serving sizes for most sodas: fruit portions are too high, but may be brought within reasonable limits by either using half of the amount of juice concentrate called for in the recipe (making a relatively dilute beverage) or by taking half servings (very small).

You will notice that many of the values are rather awkward fractions for the portions of each food group found in a given serving. This is an unfortunate but necessary consequence of trying to accurately represent the portions of each food group source found in the recipe. See Table 3 for the rough breakdown of the food group sources by composition, and Table 4 for portion sizes for fresh fruit, juices, etc.

OBESITY

Excess body fat is a major problem for many people in the United States. The average weight for most age groups, including older children, is about ten pounds higher now than it was for Americans at the turn of the century. And over 10 percent of even elementary school children are overweight. Although physiological theories abound as to the reasons for this trend, the fact is that, in the final analysis, it is our diets that are primarily responsible for most overweight. Once overweight, the body's normal homeostatic mechanisms go into operation to help keep us at whatever weight we find ourselves. Therefore, dieting is at best a somewhat uncomfortable proposition, since the body responds with hunger signals to weight-loss programs. So the question that dieters naturally ask most often is

Table 4.   Diabetics' and Dieters' Guide: Examples of Portion* Sizes
for Fruit, Bread, Fat

1 fruit portion	*1 bread portion*	*1 fat portion*
½ medium apple	1 slice whole-grain bread	1 tsp. butter
½ small banana	3 rye crisps	1 tsp. margarine
10 large cherries	1 small potato	1 tsp. oil
2 dates	½ cup cooked oatmeal	1 T heavy cream
2 T raisins	½ cup cooked rice	1 T cream cheese
⅓ cup apple juice	½ cup cooked beans	2 T sour cream
⅓ cup orange juice	⅓ cup corn	10 almonds
¼ cup prune juice	¼ cup yam	20 Spanish peanuts, in their shells

*The word "portion" is used in this cookbook the same way "exchange" or "exchange rating" is used in other books.

"How can I go hungry in the least painful way possible?" The answer to that question alone has unfortunately brought us many fad diets, often very poor in nutritional sense. So a second question must be asked: "How can I also go relatively hungry in the most healthy way possible?"

For adults and older children, I think that the answer to that question lies in eating frequently (every two to four hours) in very small portions, with the foods emphasizing first, the complex carbohydrates (needed for energy); second, low-fat animal protein sources (to meet tissue building demands); third, abundance of raw and lightly cooked vegetables (for richness in nutrients and for filling up tummies); fourth, limited amount of nutrient-rich sweets, meaning fresh fruit and low-fat sweets from this cookbook (for rounding out of nutrient supply and meeting psychological needs for sweet foods); and fifth, reliance primarily upon water as the source of liquid, with weak herb teas and weak decaffeinated coffee included in moderation for flavor variety (in order to make sure that calories come from as high-fiber, filling foods as possible). I would also suggest that you pick out your favorite high-starch, low-fat foods, and, if possible, eat the same ones day after day, planning the week's portions in advance: "gourmetdizing"* and impulse eating are the dieter's downfalls.

For children under the age of nine, reducing diets are unwise. Instead, one should work toward balanced maintenance diets that allow children to grow into their excess weight over a

*Eating a wide variety of foods.

period of one to two years. During this time, meals should be high in protein obtained as much as possible from combination of starchy (high-complex carbohydrate) and low-fat animal protein (skim milk, fish, defatted poultry, plus some eggs), ample amounts of raw vegetables, and moderate amounts of fresh fruit. Try to avoid fried foods, including potato chips and French fries. Increased physical activity is also a major factor, especially for children. Start taking brisk walks in the morning or after dinner with your overweight child (ideally, at least one-half hour long) and become involved in other physical activities that interest him or her. And when you reward or celebrate with your child, try as much as possible to do so with shared activities that do not involve food.

HYPERTENSION

There is virtually no salt used in this cookbook. Baking soda is used in breads and cakes, but the amounts are negligible (about $\frac{1}{16}$ teaspoonful per serving). I recommend the crackers in the Unsweetened Snacks section, as they are altogether devoid of salt, yet pleasantly seasoned.

CHOLESTEROL PROBLEMS

In general, oils (unsaturated fats) are used in this cookbook, and they are used in smaller proportions in these recipes as compared to most other cookbooks. The major exceptions are recipes involving large amounts of whipping cream, sour cream, cream cheese, and those which are deep-fried. These you would do well to avoid. Also, recipes which call for baking chocolate would also be better left alone, since baking chocolate is extremely high in saturated fat (cocoa powder is defatted, in contrast).

INFANCY

In my opinion, it would be optimal for infants to be exclusively breast-fed (ideally) or formula-fed, up to age six months. I base this opinion on my observation that it is at around six months that babies are able to sit up unaided, and that sitting up is an important part of being able to adequately digest solid foods. At six months, among the easiest of new foods to introduce are rice and steamed carrots. It is a good idea to stay entirely with puréed or thoroughly mashed cereals and vegetables for the next several months. Then, around age nine months, start to introduce some lumpier textures as well as fresh and lightly cooked fruit, now, for sweeter tastes. The holding off on fruit is suggested in order that sweetness not be one of the earliest, and therefore most potent, associations to eating table foods. By the end of the first year, your infant will be ready for most foods from the family table, as long as they are a manageable consistency.

As far as beverages are concerned, milk and water should be and should remain the mainstay. If you want to offer fruit juices, I suggest making them extremely dilute (about 1 tablespoon concentrate to ½ cup water). Also, the bottle should

never be used as a pacifier, nor should any liquid other than breast milk, formula, or water be associated with bedtime. One of the hazards of violating this injunction is the nursing-bottle syndrome: children actually cutting rotten teeth because they have had too many juices by bottle.

As far as protein is concerned, beyond balancing vegetable sources, among the easiest of high-protein food sources for infants to digest are yogurt and tofu (soy-bean curd). These are the main ingredients in Instant Puddings and Custards.

TODDLERHOOD

Important special considerations of toddlerhood are toddlers' relatively poor chewing ability and their on-again off-again teething discomfort. Raw vegetables are not going to be a major source of nutrition for little people with so few teeth (especially without their second set of molars in) but they are good for teething, and for developing taste habits for later on. In this cookbook, the popsicles are one food that young children in general, and teething toddlers in particular, find especially appealing. The custard-based shakes provide especially good nutrition when frozen as popsicles because of their milk and egg content.

An ordinarily good food to avoid for young toddlers is any kind of whole nut. Toddlers are too likely to swallow them without chewing, and then to choke. And a *very* undesirable food that is *particularly* undesirable for small children is chocolate. Besides its high caffeine content and other nutritional shortcomings (see Glossary), chocolate is very high in a chemical which prevents calcium from being absorbed by the body.

In other words, chocolate milk gives your child little of the calcium that is in the milk due to the oxalic acid content of the chocolate. Carob (see Glossary) is a good substitute for chocolate because it looks like chocolate. In fact, my daughter calls it "cocoa" and is well satisfied with her hot carob (see Quick Drinks under Beverages) when her friends at her sitter's house are having hot chocolate.

While toddlers tend to be very erratic eaters, I believe that it is important, as far as you are able, to keep offering (but not insisting on) lightly cooked vegetables. Do not keep fruit juices on hand, but rather encourage children to eat fresh fruit.

And last, but not least, I would like to mention the ever-loved peanut-butter and jelly sandwich, on which many American toddlers and school-age children thrive. I recommend to you the Enriched Peanut Butter (under Spreads in the Unsweetened Snacks section): it is completely nonhydrogenated, yet it does not separate out, and its sweetness and smoothness pleases even finicky little people ordinarily devoted to Skippy or Jif. The book also offers a considerable variety of jams, jellies, and butters, all delicious (under Main Dish Sweets).

KASHRUTH

For those who keep kosher, most cakes are *pareve.* * In the ones which are not, water or dilute juice may be substituted for the milk called for in the recipe. In the case of very strict observance, the use of pear-grape concentrate is not approved at this time, so you may substitute apple-juice concentrate or pineapple-juice concentrate, or a combination of the two in a 2:1 ratio, respectively, plus an extra two to three tablespoonfuls of the apple- or pineapple-juice concentrate per each one-half cup of pear-grape concentrate called for in the recipe.

*Neutral: containing neither milk nor meat products.

SECTION 1

Sweet Snacks

Candies
Cookies
Instant Puddings and Custards
Muffins
Popsicles

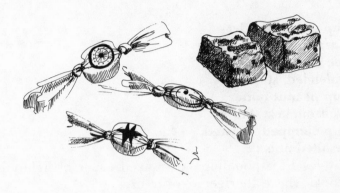

CANDIES

Carob Peanut-Butter Candy
Coconut Chewies
Frozen Bananas
Fudge
Gumdrops
Maple Fudge
Mint Creams

Instead of melting sugar and letting it harden into a recrystallized form, these recipes rely upon egg whites as the cohesive. The result is that all candies are soft instead of crunchy. Keep candies refrigerated for both preservation and correct texture. For special appeal to children, you may wrap candies individually in aluminum foil or colorful wrapping paper.

Carob Peanut-Butter Candy

2 dozen: each 101 cal., ⅓ fruit, ⅓ meat, 1 fat*

Melt in a nonstick pan
  ½ cup butter
Stir in
  **¾ cup carob powder
  (Cara-Coa, or other very
  fine grind)**
When blended, stir in
  ½ cup peanut butter
Remove from heat. Stir in
  **¾ cup chopped, roasted,
  unsalted nuts**
Drop by level teaspoonfuls onto waxed paper or lightly buttered cookie sheet. Refrigerate or freeze.

Variation: Stir in 1 cup shredded unsweetened coconut instead of nuts.

Coconut Chewies

3 dozen: each 52 cal., ¾ fruit, ½ fat

Bring to a boil in a small saucepan

1⅓ cups chopped dates (32 medium dates)	**¾ cup unsweetened apple-juice concentrate 6 T butter**

Let boil for 5 minutes.
Stir in
  1 T vanilla extract
Remove from heat. Purée in blender. While blending, add
  2 egg whites
Return to nonstick skillet over medium-high heat and stir until mixture forms a gooey ball. Let cool to lukewarm. Roll into balls about ½ inch in diameter. Roll balls in
  **¾ cup shredded
  unsweetened coconut**
Refrigerate.

*Cal. = calories; the other quantities (fruit, meat, fat) refer to diabetic "exchange ratings," explained in this book as food portions or equivalent food portions. For explanation, see Chapter 4, subsection on Diabetes and Hypoglycemia, as well as Tables 3 and 4 in that subsection.

Frozen Bananas

2 dozen: each 102 cal., 1 fruit, ¼ milk, 1 fat

Chop and set aside
  **1½ cups roasted, unsalted
    nuts**
Make a paste of
  1 cup carob powder   **½–⅔ cups evaporated
                milk***
Slice crosswise into quarters
  6 medium, firm bananas
Coat banana pieces with carob paste. Roll in chopped nuts.
Freeze. Thaw 10–20 minutes before serving.

Fudge

1½ dozen: each 81 cal., 1 fruit, ½ bread, 1 fat

Bring to a boil in a nonstick skillet
  **1 cup chopped dates (24   4 T butter or margarine
    dates)   2 oz. unsweetened dark
  ½ cup unsweetened pear-   chocolate
    grape concentrate**
Boil for 2 minutes. Stir in
  2 tsps. vanilla extract
Remove from heat. Purée in blender, beating in
  2 egg whites
Return puréed mixture to skillet over medium heat. Stir constantly until mixture forms a cohesive ball that will stick to the
spatula. Roll into small balls. Refrigerate or freeze. Serve well
chilled.

Note: People's tastes vary greatly in regard to chocolate. If
this chocolate is much too rich or chocolaty, or if you do not
like semisweet chocolate, try the following proportions: 1⅓
cups chopped dates, ¾ cup unsweetened pear-grape concentrate, 4 tsps. vanilla extract.

Variation: Mandarin Orange Fudge: Add 1 T unsweetened orange-juice concentrate.

*The amount of milk required will depend upon the grind of the carob pow-
der you use.

Gumdrops

3 dozen: each 36 cal., ½ fruit, ¼ fat

Place in a nonstick pan over low heat until gelatin is melted (about 7 minutes)

1 cup unsweetened apple-juice concentrate	**1 cup water** **10 tsps. (5 packages) gelatin**

Refrigerate for 1 hour, until partly set. Melt

¼ cup butter or margarine

Stir in

¾ cup toasted bread crumbs

Stir the bread-crumb mixture into the partly set gelatin. Transfer to a buttered bread pan. Refrigerate. When set, cut into cubes.

Variation: Add 1 tsp. grated lemon rind or grated orange rind.

Maple Fudge

2 dozen: each 64 cal., 1 fruit, ½ fat

Stir in nonstick pan over medium-high heat until butter is melted

1⅓ cups chopped dates
6 T butter
6 T molasses

Let simmer on medium heat for 5 minutes. Stir in

4 tsps. vanilla extract

Remove from heat. Purée in blender with

2 egg whites

Pour into two buttered 3-inch tart pans or large custard bowls. Bake at 350° F for 15 minutes. Cut into wedges. Refrigerate.

Mint Creams

2 dozen: each 57 cal., ½ fruit, 1 fat

Bring to a boil in a nonstick pan

1 T butter
2 T unsweetened pineapple-juice concentrate

3 T unsweetened apple-juice concentrate
½ cup date pieces (13 medium dates)

Boil vigorously for 7 minutes, stirring constantly. Transfer to blender. Purée. When lukewarm or cool, beat in

⅛ tsp. peppermint extract
8 oz. softened cream cheese

4 drops green food coloring (optional)

Spread in logs on two separate pieces of waxed paper. Fold paper over and roll. Freeze. Cut into pieces crosswise.

Peanut-Butter Chewies

3 dozen: each 38 cal., ½ fruit, ⅓ meat, ½ fat

Boil for 5 minutes over high heat

⅓ cup butter
1 cup chopped dates (24 medium dates)

¼ cup unsweetened apple-juice concentrate

Purée in blender with

2 egg whites

Stir in

1 cup nonhydrogenated peanut butter

½ cup chopped roasted peanuts

Form into small balls. Refrigerate.

COOKIES

Banana Nut Cookies
Carob Brownies
Carob Butter Cookies
Carrot Cookies
Chocolate Brownies
Chocolate Chip Cookies
Chocolate Wafer Sandwiches
Coconut Cookies
Date Bars
Gingersnaps
Hamantaschen
Lemon Butter Drops
Oatmeal-Raisin Cookies
Peanut-Butter Brownies
Peanut-Butter Cookies
Roll Dough Cookies

Like the candies, sugar-free cookies are not crunchy: Even when only date flour is used, the moisture from the dates lends softness to the cookies. Cookies are prepared in two basic ways: using date flour, or by heating juice concentrate in order that it can absorb a large volume of flour (in this way, 1 cup of concentrate plus butter or margarine is heated, and 1 cup of flour is stirred in; for extra sweetness, include some dried fruit in the hot liquid before stirring in the flour). In the cookie recipes, 1 egg is used per cup of flour in order to keep the cookies from being too crumbly. In contrast, sugar- or honey-based cookies require 1 egg per 2 cups of flour, as a rule, because the sugar or honey acts as additional cohesive.

High-protein baking: If you like the flavor, nonfat (preferably noninstant, for its smoother consistency) dry milk may be added to the recipe in volumes of up to ½ cup of dry milk per cup of flour used in the recipe. This measure may also make the cookies taste sweeter to some people.

Banana Nut Cookies

3 dozen: each 76 cal., ⅓ fruit, ⅕ bread, ⅕ milk
Purée
   1 cup banana
   5 T margarine or butter
   2 eggs
Stir into
   2 cups date flour   **1 cup chopped nuts**
   ¼ cup nonfat dry milk

Drop by teaspoonfuls onto a greased cookie sheet. Flatten. Bake at 350° F for 7–10 minutes.

Variation: Apple Nut Cookies: Substitute 1½ cups grated apple plus 1 tsp. cinnamon for the banana. Do not purée; simply beat all ingredients together.

Carob Brownies

20 brownies: each 108 cal., ½ fruit, ½ bread, 1 fat

Melt
   ½ cup margarine or
     butter
Stir in
   ¾ cup carob flour (Cara-
     Coa Powder)
Remove from heat. Mix with
   2 cups date flour
Purée
   1 cup banana
   2 eggs
Stir into flour mixture. Turn into buttered 8 × 8 × 2-inch pan. Bake 20 minutes at 350° F.

Carob Butter Cookies

2 dozen: each 88 cal., ⅓ meat, 1½ fat

(These are rich, and not very sweet.)

Melt
  ¾ cup butter
Stir in
  1 cup Cara-Coa Powder
Remove from heat. Beat in
  1 egg
Stir in
  **1 cup finely chopped
    roasted nuts**
Drop by teaspoonfuls onto an ungreased cookie sheet. Bake 10 minutes at 350° F.

Carrot Cookies

3 dozen: each 66 cal., ¼ fruit, ⅓ bread, ⅓ veg, ½ fat

Boil uncovered for 4 minutes
  2½ cups peeled, grated   **2 tsps. cinnamon**
    carrots   **½ cup margarine**
  ½ cup thawed,
    unsweetened pineapple-
    juice concentrate
Remove from heat. Stir into
  2 cups date flour
Beat in
  2 eggs
Drop by teaspoonfuls onto a greased cookie sheet. Flatten. Bake at 350° F for 10–15 minutes.

Variation: Substitute finely diced asparagus or grated zucchini for the carrots.

Chocolate Brownies

20 bars: each 256 cal., 2½ fruit, ½ bread, ½ meat, 2 fat

Bring to a boil
1 cup butter or margarine   **2½ cups chopped dates**
4 oz. unsweetened   **(60 medium dates)**
   chocolate   **¼ cup unsweetened pear-**
Stir in   **grape concentrate**
2 T vanilla extract
Purée. Cool to lukewarm. Beat in
4 eggs
Stir into
2½ cups date flour
Bake in a greased 8 × 8 × 2-inch cake pan 25–30 minutes at
350° F. Cut when cool.

Chocolate Chip Cookies

3 dozen: each 85 cal., 1 fruit, ⅓ bread, 1 fat

Prepare and freeze ahead of time
Fudge (see page 55)
Beat
2 eggs   **1 tsp. vanilla extract**
5 T oil   **1 T blackstrap molasses**
Stir into
2 cups date flour
Cut fudge into chip-sized pieces. Stir into dough. Drop by teaspoonfuls onto a greased cookie sheet. Flatten. Bake 8–10 minutes at 350° F.

Alternative: Use 1 cup melted butter or margarine instead of
oil for a much richer cookie.

Variation: Stir in 1 cup presoaked raisins instead of fudge.

Chocolate Wafer Sandwiches

3½ dozen: each 91 cal., 1½ fruit, ½ bread, 1 fat

Bring to a boil in a nonstick pan
1¼ cups unsweetened
   pear-grape concentrate

Stir in
  **6 T unsweetened cocoa
    powder**
When dissolved, stir in
  1 T vanilla extract
  **½ cup margarine or
    butter**
When butter has melted, remove from heat and stir in
  2½ cups date flour
Beat in
  2 eggs

Chill dough. Roll out between two pieces of waxed paper, using date flour to prevent sticking of dough. (See introduction to Pastries section for method.) Cut 2-inch-diameter circles. Bake at 350° F for 12–15 minutes. Cool. Spread one-half of the wafers with 1 tsp. each of
  Fudge Frosting (see page 148)
Make sandwiches using the remaining half of the wafers.

Coconut Cookies

5 dozen: each 27 cal., ½ fruit, ⅐ fat

Grind in blender, ½ cup of each at a time
  1½ cups date flour
  **1½ cups unsweetened,
    dried coconut**
Stir in a nonstick pan over medium-high heat until thick
  1 T cornstarch
  **¾ cup unsweetened
    apple-juice concentrate**
Stir in
  2 tsps. vanilla extract
Set aside. Beat until stiff
  6 egg whites
  ½ tsp. cream of tartar

Gradually add syrup to beaten egg whites, beating after each addition. Fold into the coconut flour. Drop by teaspoonfuls onto greased cookie sheet. Bake at 325° F 10–12 minutes. Let cool in oven with door ajar for 15 minutes.

Date Bars

4 dozen: each 70 cal., ½ fruit, ⅕ bread, ⅙ meat, ½ fat

Bring to a boil

10 T butter or margarine   **¾ cup chopped dates**
½ cup unsweetened   **(about 18 dates)**
   apple-juice concentrate   **2 tsps. grated lemon rind**

Stir in

¾ cup rolled oats
¼ cup raisins or currants

Stir for 2–3 minutes. Remove from heat. Beat in

4 eggs

Stir in

1 cup date flour   **½ tsp. allspice**
1 tsp. cinnamon   **1 cup chopped nuts**
¼ tsp. cloves

Spread in greased 9 × 11-inch cake pan. Bake 30 minutes at 350° F. Cut into rectangular portions.

Variations: Apricot Bars: Substitute dried apricots for the dates, golden raisins for the dark raisins.

Fig Bars: Substitute dried black mission figs for the dates, and ¼ cup unsweetened pear-grape concentrate for the corresponding amount of apple-juice concentrate.

Gingersnaps

4 dozen: each 51 cal., ⅔ fruit, ⅓ bread, ½ fat

Cream

3 cups date flour   **2 tsps. cinnamon**
6 T margarine   **¼ tsp. cloves**
3 tsps. ginger

Beat in

2 eggs
¼ cup blackstrap
   molasses
1 T apple-cider vinegar

Form dough into ¾-inch balls. Flatten. Place on a greased cookie sheet. Bake 12 minutes at 325° F.

Hamantaschen (Jewish Filled Cookies)

6 dozen: each 133 cal., ⅔ fruit, ⅓ bread, ⅓ meat, ⅔ fat

Beat
  4 eggs
  1 cup oil
  ¼ cup unsweetened
  orange-juice
  concentrate
  3 T grated orange peel

Stir into
  6 cups date flour
  ½ cup soy flour
  2 cups whole-wheat flour
Knead well. Chill dough. Roll out to about ⅓-inch thickness between two pieces of waxed paper, using date flour to prevent sticking. (See Pastries section for technique.) Cut into 3-inch diameter circles. Fill each with 2 tsps. of filling of your choice (see Strawberry Hamantaschen Filling and Fig Cookie Filling). Bake on greased cookie sheets 20–25 minutes at 350° F.

Lemon Butter Drops

2 dozen: each 89 cal., ¾ fruit, ⅓ bread, 1 fat

Cream
  ½ cup butter or
    margarine
  1½ cups date flour
Beat in
  1 egg
  2 tsps. grated lemon rind
  ½ cup unsweetened
  apple-juice concentrate
Drop from teaspoon onto greased cookie sheet well apart from one another. Bake 10 minutes at 350° F (or until rims brown).

Oatmeal-Raisin Cookies

3 dozen: each 82 cal., ⅔ fruit, 1 bread, ⅔ fat

Bring to a boil in a 2-quart pot

⅔ cup raisins

½ cup margarine

1 cup thawed, unsweetened apple-juice concentrate

Stir in mixture of

1½ cups rolled oats

1 tsp. cinnamon

⅛ tsp. cloves

⅛ tsp. nutmeg

1 tsp. vanilla extract

Remove from heat. Beat in

2 eggs

Cool to lukewarm. Stir in

1½ cups date flour

Drop by teaspoonfuls onto greased cookie sheet. Flatten. Bake 10 minutes at 350° F.

Alternative: Use 1½ cups unsweetened apple-juice concentrate; stir in ¼ cup soy flour and ½ cup whole-wheat flour along with the rolled oats; eliminate date flour.

Peanut-Butter Brownies

20 bars: each 198 cal., 1 fruit, ½ bread, ½ meat, ⅔ fat

Boil for 5 minutes

¾ cup peanut butter

¼ cup unsweetened orange-juice concentrate

¼ cup margarine

1½ cups raisins

¼ cup unsweetened apple-juice concentrate

Purée. Cool to lukewarm. Beat in

2 eggs

Stir into

1 cup date flour

Turn into buttered 8 × 8 × 2-inch baking pan. Bake 25 minutes at 350° F. Cut when cool.

Alternative: Use ½ cup unsweetened orange-juice concentrate and ½ cup unsweetened apple-juice concentrate; when boiling, stir in 6 T whole-wheat flour and 2 T soy flour. Remove from heat, and then beat in eggs. Eliminate date flour.

Variation: Peanut-Butter and Banana Brownies: Substitute water for juice concentrates; use 3 eggs; add 1½ cups mashed banana when puréeing, and an extra 1½ cups date flour. Spread on a greased cookie sheet. Bake for 20 minutes.

Peanut-Butter Cookies

4 dozen: each 102 cal., ⅓ fruit, ⅔ bread, ¼ meat, ⅓ fat

Combine
10 T butter or margarine   **1½ cups Enriched Peanut**
2 eggs   **Butter**
Stir in
3 cups date flour
Form the dough into balls. Place balls on an ungreased cookie sheet. Press flat with a fork. Bake 10 minutes at 350° F.

Alternative: Use 1 cup nonhydrogenated peanut butter instead of Enriched Peanut Butter.

Roll Dough Cookies

1 recipe* = 2,480 cal., 10 fruit, 8 bread, 3 milk, 2 meat, 12 fat

Blend
3 cups date flour   **¼ cup oil**
½ cup nonfat dry milk
Beat in
2 eggs   **3 T thawed, unsweetened**
2 tsps. vanilla extract   **apple-juice concentrate**
Knead well. Chill. Roll out to ⅓ inch thick between two pieces of waxed paper, using date flour as needed to prevent sticking. (See introduction to Pastries section for method.) Cut into desired shapes. Bake on a greased cookie sheet for 12–15 minutes at 350° F.

*For amounts per cookie, divide the number of shapes into the numbers given for the complete recipe.

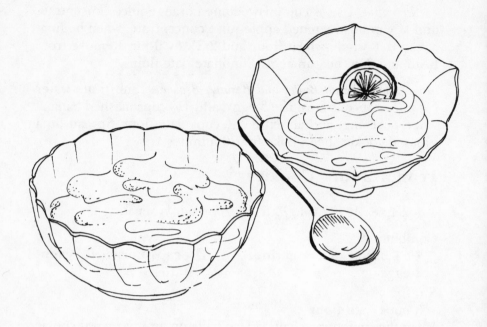

INSTANT PUDDINGS AND CUSTARDS

Banana Peanut-Butter Custard
Banana Tofu Custard
Carob Tofu Custard
Orange Yogurt Pudding
Peanut-Butter Tofu Custard
Pineapple Yogurt Pudding
Tofu Fruit Custard

Virtually any combination is possible in these snacks. They are particularly easy for toddlers and pretoddlers to handle, and both the tofu and yogurt are highly digestible—good first high-protein foods to introduce to your infant. You can create many varieties as you experiment with the different fresh or frozen fruits you have on hand, or with unsweetened fruit-juice concentrates. In creating your own puddings or custards with yogurt, you may want simply to mix in the juice concentrate, or you may want to make the pudding thicker by beating in nonfat dry milk until you reach the desired consistency.

Banana Peanut-Butter Custard

3 servings: each 181 cal., 1½ fruit, 1 milk

Purée
- 2 ripe bananas
- 2 T peanut butter
- 2 T unsweetened apple-juice concentrate
- ¼ cup nonfat dry milk

Banana Tofu Custard

3 servings: each 204 cal., 2 fruit, 1 meat, 1½ fat

Purée
- ½ lb. tofu
- 1 banana
- 3 T thawed, unsweetened apple-juice concentrate
- 2 T milk
- 2 T oil

Carob Tofu Custard

6 servings: each 151 cal., 1 fruit, 1 milk, 1 fat

Purée
- ½ lb. tofu
- ¼ cup carob powder
- ½ cup nonfat dry milk
- ¾ cup milk
- 1 cup mashed banana
- 2 T oil

Orange Yogurt Pudding

4 servings: each 145 cal., 1½ fruit, 1 milk

Beat or purée
- 1 cup plain yogurt
- 6 T thawed, unsweetened orange-juice concentrate
- 2 T thawed, unsweetened apple-juice concentrate
- ½ cup nonfat dry milk

Peanut-Butter Tofu Custard

3 servings: each 171 cal., 1 fruit, 1 milk, 2 meat

Purée

½ lb. tofu	2 T peanut butter
⅓ cup thawed, unsweetened apple-juice concentrate	2 T milk

Pineapple Yogurt Pudding

4 servings: each 135 cal., 1 fruit, 1 milk

Beat

1 cup plain yogurt	2 T thawed, unsweetened apple-juice concentrate
5 T thawed, unsweetened pineapple-juice concentrate	½ cup nonfat dry milk

Stir in

3 T unsweetened crushed pineapple (fresh or canned)

Tofu Fruit Custard

6 servings: each 128 cal., 1½ fruit, ½ meat, 1 fat

Purée

½ lb. tofu	2 T thawed, unsweetened orange-juice concentrate
2 T oil	
¼ cup thawed, unsweetened pineapple-juice concentrate	¼ cup milk
	½ banana

Stir in

1 cup chopped fruit

MUFFINS

Banana Muffins
Bran Muffins
Carrot Muffins
Cornmeal Muffins
Pumpkin Muffins
Spinach Muffins
Zucchini Apple Muffins

This section is intended to be especially convenient for preparation of snacks in preschool settings. All the muffins were enthusiastically received by my daughter's preschool classmates. The muffins seem to be a good way of including some ordinarily less-than-popular vegetables in young children's diets. For easiest clean-up, use paper muffin cups, but be sure that muffins are cool before trying to remove the paper.

Banana Muffins

2 dozen: each 70 cal., ½ fruit, ⅓ bread, ⅓ meat, ½ fat

Beat

2 cups ripe banana	**1 cup whole-wheat flour**
¼ cup oil	**½ cup soy flour**
2 eggs	**1 tsp. baking soda**
¼ cup unsweetened apple-juice concentrate	

Distribute batter evenly in greased muffin tins or paper muffin cups. Bake 20 minutes at 400° F.

Bran Muffins

3 dozen: each 79 cal., ½ fruit, ½ bread, ¼ milk, ½ fat

Let stand overnight

1 cup raisins   **2 cups milk**

Bring to a boil

1⅓ cups unsweetened   **⅔ cup oil**
  apple-juice concentrate

Pour over

3 cups bran flakes

Let stand 10 minutes. Stir in the raisins and milk. Then beat in

2 cups whole-wheat flour	**1 tsp. ginger**
½ cup soy flour	**2 tsps. cinnamon**
1½ tsps. baking soda	

Fill paper muffin cups or greased muffin tins ⅔ full. Bake at 425° F for 10–15 minutes.

Carrot Muffins

2 dozen: each 113 cal., ½ fruit, ¾ bread, ½ vegetable, 1 fat

Boil in a nonstick pan for 2 minutes

2 cups grated carrots
½ cup thawed,
  unsweetened apple-juice
  concentrate
½ cup oil

Cool to lukewarm. Stir into

2 cups whole-wheat flour
¼ cup soy flour
1 tsp. baking soda

Beat

2 eggs
½ cup milk

¼ tsp. cloves
2 tsps. cinnamon

¾ cup thawed,
unsweetened apple-juice
concentrate

Distribute evenly among paper muffin cups or greased muffin tins. Bake at 400° F for 20 minutes.

Variation: Asparagus Muffins: Substitute finely diced asparagus for carrots, and 2 tsps. grated lemon peel for cinnamon.

Cornmeal Muffins

2 dozen: each 105 cal., ½ fruit, ½ bread, ¼ milk, 1 fat

Beat

2 eggs
1 cup unsweetened apple-
juice concentrate

7 T oil
1 tsp. almond extract

Stir liquid into

1 cup cornmeal
⅔ whole-wheat flour
¼ cup soy flour

½ cup nonfat dry milk
1 tsp. baking soda

Distribute evenly in muffin tins. Bake at 425° F for 15 minutes.

Pumpkin Muffins

1½ dozen: each 82 cal., ½ fruit, ½ bread, ⅓ meat, ⅓ fat

Beat

1 cup pumpkin purée
2 eggs

¾ cup unsweetened
apple-juice concentrate

Stir liquid into

1½ cups whole-wheat
flour
¼ cup soy flour
1 tsp. baking soda

1 tsp. cinnamon
½ tsp. mace
¼ tsp. nutmeg

Stir in

¼ cup melted butter or
margarine

Distribute evenly in paper muffin cups or greased muffin tins. Bake 20 minutes at 400° F.

Spinach Muffins

2 dozen: each 84 cal., ⅓ fruit, ½ bread, ½ meat, ¼ fat

Boil for 2 minutes
1 lb. chopped spinach,   **pineapple-juice**
  frozen or fresh   **concentrate**
⅓ cup oil   **½ cup unsweetened**
¼ cup unsweetened   **apple-juice concentrate**

Remove from heat. Cool slightly. Stir into
1½ cups rye flour   **1 tsp. dried chervil**
½ cup soy flour   **1 tsp. cinnamon**
⅓ cup nonfat dry milk   **¼ tsp. nutmeg**
1 tsp. baking soda
Beat in
2 eggs
Pour into individual muffin tins or paper muffin cups, distributing evenly. Bake for 15 minutes at 375° F.

Zucchini Apple Muffins

2 dozen: each 84 cal., ½ fruit, ⅓ bread, ⅓ meat, ½ fat

Grate enough apple and zucchini to make
1 cup grated apple,   **1 cup grated zucchini,**
  packed (peeling   **packed**
  optional)
Beat
2 eggs
⅔ cup unsweetened
  apple-juice concentrate
Stir liquid into
1¼ cups whole-wheat   **½ cup soy flour**
  flour   **1 tsp. baking soda**
Stir in the grated zucchini and apple, followed by
¼ cup melted butter or   **½ cup chopped roasted**
  margarine   **nuts**

Distribute evenly among paper baking cups or greased muffin tins. Bake for 20 minutes at 400° F.

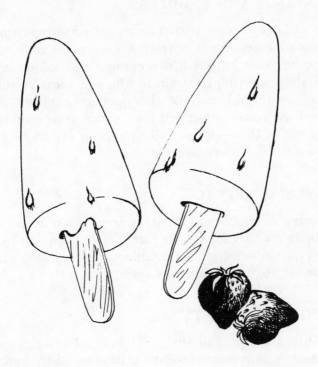

POPSICLES

Apple Popsicles
Banana Yogurt Popsicles
Blueberry Popsicles
Carob Pudding Pops
Fudgesicles
Orange Popsicles
Strawberry Popsicles
Yogurt Northern-Fruit Popsicles
Yogurt Tropical-Fruit Popsicles

These were a major hit in our neighborhood. "Customers"—primarily ages three through six—returned again and again. The proportions in the recipes are designed for extra sweetness to entice sugar-accustomed palates. The serving size is based on the Tupperware popsicle container, which holds about ¼ cup of liquid.

FOR INFANTS AND TODDLERS

Infants and toddlers are particularly pleased with anything frozen on a stick because it is relatively easy to handle and can help soothe gums inflamed by teething. With infants and toddlers, I suggest trying to minimize the sweetness by substituting some water for part of the juice concentrate. For my toddler, I use considerably less juice concentrate than is called for in some of the recipes—and she seems just as happy with them as when they were sweeter.

FOR SPECIAL APPEAL

Try pouring different-colored liquid from two different recipes in alternating layers for frozen-parfait-style pops. For example, blueberry, then strawberry, then blueberry; or carob pudding, then banana yogurt, then carob again.

FOR INFINITE VARIETY

Quick Drinks, Soups, and Shakes, as well as Puddings and Custards (the last must be puréed first with some added milk or water), may all be frozen into popsicles.

Note: If a popsicle stick comes out of the popsicle before serving, pour a very small amount of water into the popsicle-stick hole, reinsert stick, and refreeze.

Apple Popsicles

8 popsicles: each 40 cal., 1 fruit

Combine
⅔ cup thawed,   **1⅓ cups water**
unsweetened apple-juice
concentrate
Pour into popsicle containers. Freeze.

Variation: Grape Popsicles: Substitute unsweetened pear-grape concentrate for apple-juice concentrate.

Banana Yogurt Popsicles

8 popsicles: each 30 cal., ⅔ fruit, ¼ milk

Purée or mash enough bananas to equal
1 cup mashed banana   **2 T thawed, unsweetened**
Beat in with   **apple-juice concentrate**
⅓ cup plain yogurt
½ cup milk
Freeze into popsicles.

Blueberry Popsicles

8 popsicles: each 33 cal., 1 fruit
(Terrifically messy—and delicious!)

Purée
1 cup fresh or thawed
blueberries
Mix with
⅓ cup thawed,   **⅔ cup water**
unsweetened pear-grape
concentrate
Freeze into popsicles.

Variations: Cherry: Substitute pitted dark cherries for blueberries.
Peach: Substitute peeled, diced peaches for blueberries and 3 T apple-juice concentrate plus 3 T pineapple-juice concentrate for pear-grape concentrate.

Fudgesicles

8 popsicles: each 63 cal., 1 fruit, ¼ milk

Measure and set aside
**3 T unsweetened cocoa
powder**
Bring to a boil in a nonstick pan
**½ cup thawed,   1 tsp. butter
unsweetened pear-grape
concentrate**
When liquid is at a full boil, stir in the cocoa until dissolved.
Remove from heat and let cool to lukewarm. Beat in
1½ cups milk
Freeze into popsicles.

Orange Popsicles

8 popsicles: each 42 cal., 1 fruit

Combine
**½ cup thawed,   3 T thawed, unsweetened
unsweetened orange-   apple-juice concentrate
juice concentrate   1⅓ cups water**
Freeze into popsicles.

Variation: Pineapple: Substitute unsweetened pineapple-juice
concentrate for the orange-juice concentrate.

Strawberry Popsicles

12 popsicles: each 44 cal., 1 fruit

Purée
**1 cup strawberries   1 cup thawed,
1 cup water   unsweetened apple-juice
concentrate**

Freeze into popsicles.

Yogurt Northern-Fruit Popsicles

6 popsicles: each 40 cal., 1 fruit, ⅕ milk

Beat or blend at low speed
    ½ cup plain yogurt   **½ cup thawed,**
    ½ cup water   **unsweetened apple-juice**
    2 T nonfat dry milk   **or pear-grape**
                            concentrate

Stir gently to eliminate air bubbles. Freeze into popsicles.

Yogurt Tropical-Fruit Popsicles

6 popsicles: each 68 cal., 1 fruit, ¼ milk

Beat or blend at low speed
    ½ cup plain yogurt   **¼ cup nonfat dry milk**
    ½ cup water   **5 T thawed, unsweetened**
    3 T thawed, unsweetened   **orange- or pineapple-**
      apple-juice concentrate   **juice concentrate**

Stir gently to eliminate air. Freeze into popsicles.

SECTION **2**

Beverages

Quick Drinks
Shakes
Sodas

QUICK DRINKS

Banana Breakfast
Blueberry Smoothie
Cool-Aid
Fresh Fruit Drink
Frosted Coffee
Hot Carob
Hot Cider
Melon Drink
Melon Slush
Orange Cream
Peach Colada
Peanut Milk
Raspberry Frappé
Strawberry-Orange Milk

Banana Breakfast

2 servings: each 176 cal., 2 fruit, 1 milk

Purée in blender
1 egg   **3 T thawed, unsweetened**
1 ripe banana   **apple-juice concentrate**
Beat in
1 cup milk
Serve immediately.

Variation: Carob Banana Breakfast: Purée 3 T carob powder along with banana; eliminate apple-juice concentrate.

Blueberry Smoothie

6 servings: each 84 cal., 2 fruit

Peel, slice and freeze
2 ripe medium bananas
When ready to serve, purée in blender with
2 cups fresh or frozen   **¼ cup unsweetened pear-**
blueberries   **grape concentrate**
                                   1 cup crushed ice

Cool-Aid

4 servings: each 90 cal., 2 fruit

(None of the "teas" is caffeinated. Red Zinger is high in vitamin C; camomile is a mild relaxant; peppermint tea aids digestion; comfrey is helpful to the entire gastrointestinal tract, and can even reduce or stop diarrhea for some people.)

Steep for 10 minutes
2 tsps. Red Zinger tea   **1 cup boiling water**
1 T camomile tea
Strain. Dilute with
¾ cup unsweetened   **3 cups ice water**
apple-juice concentrate

Variation: Substitute 1 tsp. dried peppermint leaves for the Red Zinger, and 1 T comfrey tea for the camomile.

Fresh Fruit Drink

6 servings: each 138 cal., 2½ fruit, ½ milk

Soak overnight (12–24 hours)
½ cup dates or raisins   **2 cups milk**
Place the soaked fruit in blender with
2 cups blueberries or   **12 ice cubes, crushed**
pitted dark cherries
Purée. Stir in the milk. Serve immediately.

Variation: Substitute strawberries or peeled peaches or apricots for the blueberries.

Frosted Coffee

4 servings: each 145 cal., 2½ fruit, ½ milk

Combine
2 tsps. instant   **2 T boiling water**
decaffeinated coffee
Purée in blender with
2 ripe medium bananas   **⅓ cup unsweetened**
1 cup crushed ice   **pineapple-juice**
concentrate

Stir in
1½ cups milk

Hot Carob

1 serving: 44 cal., ½ milk

Combine
2 tsps. Cara-Coa powder   **½ cup boiling water**
Add
½ cup milk
Serve immediately. This drink is also delicious cold.

Hot Cider

6 servings: each 100 cal., 2½ fruit

Bring to a boil

**4 cups bottled or canned
    apple juice**
**¼ cup thawed,
    unsweetened orange-
    juice concentrate**

**2 T thawed, unsweetened
    apple-juice concentrate**
1 cinnamon stick
1 tsp. oil.

Cover, reduce heat, and simmer 5 minutes. Serve hot.

Melon Drink

4 servings: each 77 cal., 2 fruit

Purée in blender

3½ cups cantaloupe
**¼ cup unsweetened
    apple-juice concentrate**

**1 T unsweetened orange-
    juice concentrate**

Variations: 1. Substitute honeydew for cantaloupe, and unsweetened pineapple-juice concentrate for orange-juice concentrate.

2. Substitute watermelon for cantaloupe, and unsweetened pear-grape concentrate for apple-juice concentrate.

Melon Slush

4 servings: each 44 cal., 1 fruit

Purée

**3 cups diced watermelon,
    honeydew, or
    cantaloupe**
1 cup crushed ice

1 T lemon juice
**2 T unsweetened
    pineapple-juice
    concentrate**

Orange Cream

3 servings: each 154 cal., 2½ fruit, ½ milk

Place in blender on high speed

**½ cup thawed,
  unsweetened orange-
  juice concentrate
1 cup buttermilk**

**3 T thawed, unsweetened
  apple-juice concentrate
6 ice cubes, crushed**

Variation: Pineapple Cream: Substitute unsweetened pineapple-juice concentrate for orange-juice concentrate.

Peach Colada

4 servings: each 160 cal., 2 fruit, 1 fat

Purée

**½ cup canned
  unsweetened coconut
  cream
½ cup water
1½ cups peeled and diced
  peaches, fresh or frozen**

**⅓ cup unsweetened
  pineapple-juice
  concentrate
2 cups crushed ice**

Variation: Piña Colada: Substitute fresh or canned unsweetened pineapple for peaches.

Peanut Milk

3 servings: each 174 cal., 1½ fruit, ½ milk

Beat at medium speed in blender until smooth

**1½ cups milk
2 T nonfat dry milk
2 T peanut butter
1 ripe medium banana**

**¼ cup thawed,
  unsweetened apple-juice
  concentrate**

Raspberry Frappé

4 servings: each 116 cal., 2½ fruit

Purée in blender

1 cup fresh or frozen raspberries
1 cup crushed ice
½ cup unsweetened orange-juice concentrate
¼ cup unsweetened pineapple-juice concentrate

Stir in

2 cups ice water

Variation: Steep ¼ tsp. dried peppermint leaves in ½ cup boiling water; substitute this for equal amount of ice water.

Strawberry Orange Milk

3 servings: each 98 cal., 1½ fruit, ½ milk

Blend until smooth

¼ cup unsweetened orange-juice concentrate
1 T unsweetened apple-juice concentrate
1 cup fresh or frozen strawberries
1 cup milk

SHAKES

Banana Milk Shake
Carob Milk Shake
Chocolate Milk Shake
Eggnog Milk Shake
Pineapple Milk Shake
Strawberry Milk Shake

These shakes are basically milk sauces or custards. They must be prepared in advance for thorough chilling. After puréeing, they remain thick, and therefore may be either consumed immediately or stored in the refrigerator for several days. In making cream sauces, arrowroot powder is recommended over cornstarch because it does not have a floury taste. The consistency of the shakes may be varied according to your preference by the amount of water or milk you use when puréeing the chilled sauce or custard. The sweetness may be increased at the time of puréeing, if you wish, by using a juice concentrate instead of some of the milk or water.

Banana Milk Shake

3 servings: each 267 cal., 2 fruit, 1 bread, 1 milk

Stir over medium heat until thick

2 cups milk
4 T cornstarch or
arrowroot powder

6 T nonfat dry milk

Chill. Purée with

1 cup mashed banana
(2 medium bananas)

2 T unsweetened apple-
juice concentrate
⅓ cup milk

Carob Milk Shake

4 servings: each 240 cal., 3 fruit, 2 milk, 1 fat

Soak overnight

4 cups milk
1½ cups chopped raisins

Strain, pressing all the liquid out of the raisins. Add enough milk to again equal 4 cups. Reserve the raisin purée for use in Brownies. Beat in with liquid

¾ cup carob powder
(Cara-Coa powder)

4 eggs
½ tsp. nutmeg

Bake in oiled 1½-quart baking dish at 350° F for 30–40 minutes. Chill. Purée with

1 cup mashed banana

adding water or milk 1 tablespoon at a time until desired consistency is reached.

Chocolate Milk Shake

6 servings: each 260 cal., 3 fruit, 1 milk, 1 meat, ⅓ fat

Beat

1¼ cups unsweetened
pear-grape concentrate
½ cup nonfat dry milk

7 T unsweetened cocoa
powder
4 cups milk
4 eggs

Bake in oiled 1-quart baking dish at 350° F for 30–40 minutes. Chill. When ready to serve, purée, adding water or milk 1 tablespoon at a time until desired consistency is reached.

Variation: Purée 1 cup custard with 1 cup mashed banana; then beat in remainder of custard along with added liquid.

Eggnog Milk Shake

6 servings: each 203 cal., 1½ fruit, 1 milk, 1 meat

Beat

4 eggs
4 cups milk
¾ cup unsweetened apple-juice concentrate

1 T vanilla extract
½ tsp. nutmeg
½ cup nonfat dry milk

Bake in oiled 1½-quart baking dish at 350° F for 30–40 minutes. Chill. Purée with enough milk or water to reach desired consistency.

Alternative: A much richer shake can be obtained by substituting 1 cup evaporated milk for corresponding amount of skim milk.

Pineapple Milk Shake

6 servings: each 250 cal., 3 fruit, 1 milk, ½ meat, ½ fat

Beat

4 cups pineapple juice
1 cup nonfat dry milk

4 eggs

Bake in oiled 1½-quart baking dish at 350° F for 30–40 minutes. Chill. Purée with

¼ cup unsweetened pineapple-juice concentrate

¼ cup unsweetened apple-juice concentrate

Strawberry Milk Shake

6 servings: each 166 cal., 2 fruit, 1 milk

Beat

5 egg whites
1 cup milk
1 cup unsweetened apple-juice concentrate

2 cups puréed strawberries
½ cup nonfat dry milk

Bake 30–40 minutes at 350° F in oiled 1½-quart baking dish. Chill. Purée with enough milk or water to reach desired consistency.

Variation: Blueberry: Substitute blueberries for strawberries; pear-grape concentrate for apple-juice concentrate.

SODAS

Coffee Soda (Cola)
Cream Soda
Hawaiian Punch
Lemon-Lime Soda
Grape Soda
"Lemon" Cola
Light Root Beer
Nonalcoholic Champagne

Most commercially available sodas, including diet sodas and club soda—with the exception of mineral and "salt-free" sodas—are extremely high in sodium content. The optimum source of carbonated water in terms of health and long-range monetary costs is to make seltzer at home using ice water and a carbon-dioxide charging system. Recipes here, however, are written for club soda, since this is the most readily available and inexpensive carbonated water. One bottle of club soda contains 1 pint, 12 ounces of soda, or 3½ cups.

As you and your family wean yourselves away from sugar, I suggest gradually reducing the proportion of juice concentrate to as little as ⅓ or ¼ the amount in the recipe (except in coffee-containing sodas, in which the juice concentrate is needed to offset the bitterness of the coffee; in those, simply make the solutions more dilute by adding more of the soda or seltzer water, and sharing the beverage).

DIABETICS

Use ⅔ to ½ the amount of juice concentrate called for in the recipe, in order to keep the number of fruit portions at or below 2 per serving; for coffee-containing sodas, either drink just ½ serving (very small indeed) or add twice the volume of club soda and divide the number of servings by 2, or reduce both the coffee and the juice concentrate by half.

Coffee Soda (Cola)

1 serving: each 155 cal., 4 fruit
Combine

2 tsps. instant decaffeinated coffee	**1 T boiling water**

Stir in

2 T thawed, unsweetened pear-grape concentrate	**3 T thawed, unsweetened apple-juice concentrate**
	½ tsp. vanilla extract

Pour mixture down side of glass (to prevent excess foaming) of
⅔ cup club soda
This recipe can be made in larger quantities, but should be assembled by the glass because fizz is lost in transferring the soda from one container to another, and because coffee causes excess foaming when mixed with juice concentrates.

Cream Soda

1 serving: 120 cal., 3 fruit

Combine

¼ cup thawed, unsweetened apple-juice concentrate	**¼ tsp. vanilla extract**
	¾ cup club soda

For a large volume, combine

1 cup plus 3 T thawed, unsweetened apple-juice concentrate	**1¼ tsps. vanilla extract**
	1 bottle of club soda

Hawaiian Punch

10 servings: each 64 cal., 1½ fruit

Purée in blender

⅔ cup thawed, unsweetened pineapple-juice concentrate	**1 cup chopped fresh or frozen strawberries**
2 oranges, peeled, seeded, and membranes removed	**¼ cup thawed, unsweetened apple-juice concentrate**

When ready to serve, fill punch bowl with ice. Pour liquid over ice, followed by
1 bottle of club soda

Lemon-Lime Soda

1 serving: 120 cal., 3 fruit

Combine

1 tsp. fresh lemon juice
1 tsp. fresh lime juice
⅔ cup club soda

¼ cup thawed, unsweetened apple-juice concentrate

For a large volume, combine

5¼ tsps. fresh lemon juice
5¼ tsps. fresh lime juice
1 bottle of club soda

1⅓ cups thawed, unsweetened apple-juice concentrate

Grape Soda

1 serving: 130 cal., 3½ fruit

Combine

¼ cup thawed, unsweetened pear-grape concentrate

⅔ cup club soda

For a large volume, combine

1⅓ cups thawed, unsweetened pear-grape concentrate

1 bottle of club soda

"Lemon" Cola

1 serving: 180 cal., 4¼ fruit

Combine

2 tsps. instant decaffeinated coffee

1 T boiling water

Combine with

5 T thawed, unsweetened apple-juice concentrate

1 T thawed, unsweetened orange-juice concentrate

Pour mixture down side of glass (to prevent excessive foaming) of

⅔ cup club soda

As with the Coffee Soda, the coffee in this recipe causes extra foaming; therefore, even large quantities should be assembled by the glass.

Light Root Beer

1 serving: 117 cal., 3½ fruit

Combine
½ tsp. instant   **1 tsp. boiling water**
  decaffeinated coffee
Combine with
2 T prune juice
3 T thawed, unsweetened   **1 tsp. thawed,**
  apple-juice concentrate   **unsweetened orange-**
⅛ tsp. vanilla extract   **juice concentrate**
                                      ½ cup club soda

Nonalcoholic Champagne

1 serving: 120 cal., 3 fruit

Combine
2 T thawed, unsweetened   **2 T thawed, unsweetened**
  apple-juice concentrate   **orange-juice**
⅔ cup club soda   **concentrate**

For a large volume, combine
⅔ cup thawed,   **⅔ cup thawed,**
  unsweetened apple-juice   **unsweetened orange-**
  concentrate   **juice concentrate**
                                      1 bottle of club soda

3

Main-Meal Sweets

Breads
Jams, Jellies, and Butters
Pancakes, Fritters, Etc.
Sauces and Syrups
Soups

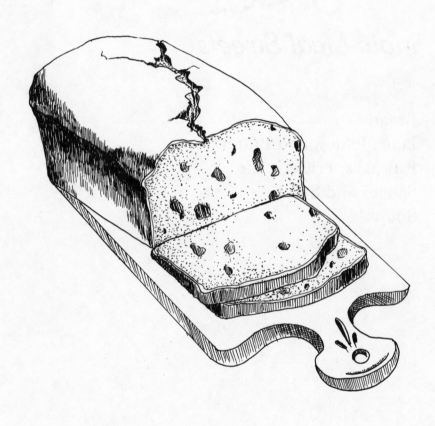

BREADS

Banana Bread, Baked
Banana Bread, Steamed
Blueberry Bread
Brown Bread
Carob Doughnuts
Chocolate Doughnuts
Date-Nut Bread
Raisin-Oat Bread
Spiced Pumpkin Loaf
Strukla (Noodle Strudel)
Whole-Wheat Doughnuts

In this section, doughnuts as well as a noodle strudel are included. *Caution:* There is no way that deep-fried doughnuts can be good for you. They are extremely high in partially saturated fat content, because frying even in an unsaturated oil causes partial hydrogenation of the oil. But at least they are "less bad" than the sugar-and-white-flour varieties.

DIABETICS AND CHOLESTEROL WATCHERS

Avoid the deep-fried doughnuts altogether, or bake them as recommended for the Carob Doughnuts. The steamed breads are particularly suited to your diets, as they contain no fat whatsoever.

Banana Bread, Baked

12 slices: each 209 cal., 1½ fruit, 1 bread, 1 veg, ½ meat, 1 fat

Beat

2 ripe, mashed bananas	**¼ cup unsweetened**
2 cups date flour	**apple-juice concentrate**
½ cup brown rice	**1 tsp. baking soda**
¼ cup nonfat dry milk	**¼ tsp. salt**
¼ cup milk	

Stir in

1 cup chopped nuts

Bake in a well-greased 9 × 5-inch loaf pan at 325° F for about 1 hour. Turn oven off and let stand in oven for 30 minutes.

Banana Bread, Steamed

16 half-slices: each 68 cal., ½ fruit, ⅔ bread

Mix

¾ cup cornmeal	**¼ cup soy flour**
½ cup whole-wheat flour	**1 tsp. baking soda**

Purée

⅔ cup yogurt	**⅓ cup unsweetened**
1 cup mashed banana	**apple-juice concentrate**
1 tsp. vanilla extract	**¼ tsp. cinnamon**
	¹⁄₁₆ tsp. nutmeg

Stir wet ingredients into dry ingredients. Pour into a buttered 2-pound can mold. Tie well-oiled brown paper on can as tightly as possible as a cover. Steam for 1½–2 hours in a large, tightly covered pot containing boiling water to one-half the height of the can. Replenish water as needed.

Blueberry Bread

16 half-slices: each 62 cal., $\frac{1}{2}$ fruit, $\frac{1}{2}$ bread

Beat

**$\frac{1}{2}$ cup unsweetened
apple-juice concentrate
1 egg
$\frac{1}{3}$ cup milk
1 tsp. grated orange rind**

**$\frac{3}{4}$ cup whole-wheat flour
$\frac{1}{4}$ cup soy flour
$\frac{3}{4}$ cup toasted whole-
grain bread crumbs
1 tsp. baking soda**

Pour one-half of batter into a buttered 2-pound can mold. Stir in

**1 cup fresh or thawed
blueberries**

Steam as indicated for Banana Bread, Steamed.

Brown Bread

16 half-slices: each 81 cal., $\frac{2}{3}$ fruit, $\frac{2}{3}$ bread

Soak overnight

1 cup raisins   **$1\frac{1}{4}$ cups milk**

Mix with

**$\frac{1}{4}$ cup unsweetened
apple-juice concentrate
$\frac{3}{4}$ cup cornmeal
$\frac{1}{2}$ cup whole-wheat flour**

**$\frac{1}{4}$ cup rye flour
$\frac{1}{2}$ tsp. cinnamon
1 tsp. baking soda**

Pour into a buttered 2-pound can mold. Steam as indicated for Banana Bread, Steamed.

Carob Doughnuts

2 dozen: each 80 cal., 1 fruit, $\frac{2}{3}$ bread, $\frac{1}{3}$ fat

Let stand

1 package dry active yeast   **2 T warm water**

Boil

**2 T oil
$\frac{3}{4}$ cup prune juice**

Stir into mixture of

**$1\frac{1}{2}$ cups date flour
$\frac{1}{2}$ cup whole-wheat flour**

**$\frac{1}{2}$ cup carob flour
$\frac{1}{2}$ tsp. nutmeg**

Stir in the yeast. Beat in

**2 egg whites at room
temperature**

Cover. Let rise in a warm place until double in bulk, about 1 hour. Roll out dough to ½-inch thickness between two pieces of waxed paper, using carob powder to prevent sticking. Cut with doughnut cutter floured with carob flour. Transfer to a well-greased cookie sheet. Brush with melted margarine or butter. Let rise 20 minutes. Bake at 425° F for 8–10 minutes. Brush immediately with more melted butter or margarine.

Chocolate Doughnuts

4 dozen: each 76+ cal., ⅓ fruit, ¾ bread, more than 3 fat*

Beat
2 eggs   **2 T vanilla extract**
1⅓ cups lukewarm milk
Stir in
6 T melted butter
Stir into
3 cups date flour   **6 T unsweetened cocoa**
1 cup whole-wheat flour   **powder**
1 cup soy flour   **2 T baking powder**
1 cup brown rice flour   **¼ tsp. cinnamon**

Knead dough as little as possible. Roll out between two pieces of waxed paper to about ½-inch thickness. Cut with floured doughnut cutter. Let stand for 10 minutes. Deep-fry at 355°–375° F. Drop into hot oil top side down. As doughnuts rise to the surface, turn them over with a slotted utensil. Fry until golden brown. Drain on paper towels.

Date-Nut Bread

16 pieces: each 163 cal., 1 fruit, 1 bread, ½ milk, ½ fat

Soak overnight
2 cups milk   **¾ cup chopped dates**
Stir into
⅔ cup date flour   **½ cup chopped nuts**
½ cup quick-cooking oats   **2 tsps. baking soda**
2 cups whole-wheat flour
Beat in
2 T unsweetened apple-   **6 T unsweetened**
juice concentrate   **pineapple-juice**
2 eggs   **concentrate**

*For fat absorbed in frying, at least 100 calories may be added to the calorie figure.

Pour into a buttered shallow 1½-quart casserole dusted lightly with

1 T toasted wheat germ

Bake at 350° F for 50–60 minutes. Cover the loaf with aluminum foil after 30 minutes in order to prevent overbrowning.

Raisin-Oat Bread

24 slices: each 202 cal., 1 fruit, 1½ bread, ½ meat, ⅓ fat

Soak overnight

2 cups raisins   **2 cups water**

Place in a pan in the oven at 200° F

1½ cups rolled oats

Drain the water from the raisins. Combine the water with

¾ cup unsweetened   **Enough boiling water to**
apple-juice concentrate   **equal a total of 4 cups**
                                                      liquid

Stir in raisins. When water is about 120° F, stir in

3 packages yeast

Let stand in a warm place until foamy (about 10 minutes). Stir in the warm oatmeal along with

¼ cup oil   **½ tsp. salt**

Let stand for about 5 minutes. Preheat oven to 275° F. Stir in

¼ cup wheat germ   **5 cups whole-wheat flour**
1 cup soy grits

Knead until elastic, adding another

1 cup whole-wheat flour

while kneading. Distribute between two greased 9 × 5-inch loaf pans. Bake for 15 minutes at 275° F, followed by 30–40 minutes at 350° F.

Spiced Pumpkin Loaf

12 slices: each 219 cal., 2 fruit, 1 bread, ⅔ meat, 1 fat

Blend

1 cup canned pumpkin
½ cup thawed,
unsweetened pineapple-
juice concentrate

½ cup thawed,
unsweetened apple-juice
concentrate
2 eggs

Stir into

2 cups date flour
¼ cup soy flour
½ cup brown rice or
whole-wheat flour
1 tsp. baking soda
¼ tsp. salt

½ tsp. ginger
½ tsp. mace
1 tsp. cinnamon
¼ tsp. nutmeg
⅛ tsp. cloves
⅔ cup chopped nuts

Transfer to a greased 9 × 5-inch loaf pan. Bake at 325°F for 50 minutes. Turn off oven. Let stand in oven for 30 minutes.

Strukla (Noodle Strudel)

12 servings: each 292 cal., 1 fruit, 1 bread, 1 meat, 1 fat

Beat until light

4 eggs

Stir into

1¼ cups whole-wheat
flour

½ cup soy flour
6 T date flour
⅛ tsp. nutmeg

Knead until hard and elastic. If too dry, add

⅔ T water

Roll out dough with a floured rolling pin into an oval shape on a lightly floured surface. Spread about ¼ inch thick with a mixture of

2⅓ cups small-curd
cottage cheese
2 tsps. cinnamon
1 T dried chervil

1 T dried chives
3 T dried parsley
¾ cup chopped dates (18
medium dates)

Leave ¼ inch uncovered all around the perimeter of the dough. Roll up as you would a strudel and seal by dampening with water lengthwise. Coil strudel and roll up in a thin cloth. Immerse in boiling water for 45 minutes. While Strukla is cooking, lightly sauté

1½ cups fresh whole-grain bread crumbs	**6 T date flour**
	6 T butter or margarine

When Strukla is done, roll out onto a platter. Sprinkle with crumb mixture. Serve hot.

Whole-Wheat Doughnuts

4 dozen: each 70+ cal., ⅓ fruit, ⅔ bread, more than 3 fat*

Beat

2 eggs	**½ tsp. vanilla extract**
1¼ cups lukewarm milk	**6 T melted butter**

Stir into

3¼ cups flour	**1 tsp. cinnamon**
2½ cups date flour	**1 tsp. nutmeg**
2 T baking powder	

Work dough quickly so that gluten cannot develop. Roll out dough between two pieces of waxed paper to about ⅓ inch thick. Follow the instructions as for the Chocolate Doughnuts.

*Deep-frying adds over 100 calories to figure given; without deep-frying, doughnuts would contain only about ⅓ fat portion each.

JAMS, JELLIES, and BUTTERS

Apple Butter
Apple Jelly
Apricot Jam
Date Butter
Date Jam
Grape Jelly
Indian Chutney
Orange Marmalade
Raspberry Jam
Strawberry Jam

If a jam is not sweet enough for your family's taste, substitute some of the juice called for in the recipe for the water. If you make peanut-butter and jelly sandwiches, I recommend using the Enriched Peanut Butter (see Unsweetened Snacks: Spreads, page 211), which is very sweet, yet contains no fruit, and is much smoother than plain nonhydrogenated peanut butter.

GOURMET SERVING SUGGESTIONS

Use jams or jellies to make ice-cream sundaes and parfaits, or as filling for layer and split-layer cakes (see Cakes, pages 127–137).

Apple Butter

1½ cups: each T 26 cal., ½ fruit

Boil vigorously for 7 minutes, covered,

1 cup grated apple,
packed
½ cup unsweetened
apple-juice concentrate

1 T margarine or butter
¼ tsp. cinnamon
⅛ tsp. cloves

Purée. Refrigerate.

Apple Jelly

1¼ cups: each T 14 cal., ⅓ fruit

Boil for 1 minute, stirring constantly

½ cup thawed,
unsweetened apple-juice
concentrate

¼ cup unsweetened
bottled red grape juice
½ cup water
5 tsps. Slimset*

Pour immediately into a clean jar. Refrigerate.

Apricot Jam

2 cups: each T 31 cal., ⅔ fruit

Bring to a boil in a small saucepan

2 cups dried apricots
1 tsp. oil
½ cup water
¼ tsp. grated orange rind

½ cup thawed,
unsweetened apple-juice
concentrate
1 cinnamon stick

Cover. Reduce heat and simmer for 15 minutes. Remove cinnamon stick. Purée.

Variations: Fig: Substitute figs for apricots. *Prune:* Substitute prunes for apricots; eliminate orange rind.

*A no-sugar jelling mix, available at supermarkets.

Date Butter

1¼ cups: each T 52 cal., 1 fruit, ½ fat

In a small saucepan, bring to a boil

**1 cup chopped dates (24
    medium dates)**
**¼ cup unsweetened
    apple-juice concentrate**

**1 T unsweetened orange-
    juice concentrate**
½ tsp. grated lemon rind
**¼ cup margarine or
    butter**

Reduce heat and simmer covered for 10 minutes. Purée. Refrigerate. Serve chilled.

Date Jam (Sephardic "Charoseth")

1¼ cups: each T 35 cal., 1 fruit

Bring to a boil in a nonstick pan

**1 cup chopped dates (24
    medium dates)**
2 tsps. cinnamon

½ cup water
**¼ cup unsweetened
    apple-juice concentrate**

Continue to cook on high heat for 5 minutes, uncovered. Let cool slightly, and stir in

**2 T finely chopped
    walnuts**

Refrigerate.

Grape Jelly

1¼ cups: each T 19 cal., ½ fruit

Combine in a nonstick pan

**¾ cup thawed,
    unsweetened pear-grape
    concentrate**

½ cup water
5 tsps. Slimset*

Place over burner on high heat. Bring to a boil. Let boil 1 minute, stirring constantly. Remove from heat; pour immediately into a clean jar or glass. Cover and refrigerate.

*See footnote, page 107.

Indian Chutney

4 cups: each T 20 cal., ½ fruit

Bring to a boil

6 T unsweetened apple-juice concentrate
1½ cups golden raisins, chopped or ground
3 cups peaches or mangoes
1 T grated orange rind
½ cup chopped red or white onions

1 tsp. cinnamon
2 tsps. ginger
½ tsp. cloves
2 T apple-cider vinegar
1/16 tsp. red pepper
1 T oil

Reduce heat to medium and let cook until most of liquid has evaporated (10–15 minutes). Refrigerate, or pour into prepared canning jars and seal.

Orange Marmalade

2½ cups: each T 24 cal., ½ fruit

Bring to a boil in a nonstick pan

1 T grated orange peel
½ cup chopped golden raisins
¾ cup unsweetened apple-juice concentrate

1½ cups diced orange sections, membranes removed
1 tsp. oil

Cover. Cook over high heat for 5 minutes. Stir in

½ cup unsweetened orange-juice concentrate

10 tsps. Slimset*

Bring to a boil. Stir for 1 minute. Pour immediately into clear jar or glass. Cover and refrigerate.

*See footnote, page 107.

Raspberry Jam

2¼ cups: each T 14 cal., ⅓ fruit

Purée
- **¾ lb. fresh or thawed raspberries (about 1½ cups purée)**
- **¾ cup unsweetened apple-juice concentrate**
- **1 T unsweetened pineapple-juice concentrate**
- **½ cup water**

Pour into a nonstick pan. Stir in
- **3 T Slimset***

Place over burner on high. Bring to a boil, and let boil for 1 minute, stirring constantly. Pour into clean glass or jar. Cover and refrigerate.

Strawberry Jam

1⅓ cups: each T 13 cal., ⅓ fruit

Purée
- **½ lb. fresh or thawed strawberries (about ⅔ cup purée)**
- **6 T unsweetened apple-juice concentrate**
- **2 T unsweetened orange-juice concentrate**
- **5 T water**

Pour into a nonstick pan. Stir in
- **2 T Slimset***

Place over burner on high. Bring to a boil. Boil for 1 minute, stirring constantly. Pour immediately into a glass or jar. Cover and refrigerate.

*See footnote, page 107

PANCAKES, FRITTERS, ETC.

Apple Fritters or Pancakes
Banana Fritters
Blueberry Pancakes
Buttermilk Pancakes
Carob French Toast
Cinnamon French Toast
Cottage-Cheese Pancakes
Matsoh Brei Pancakes
Orange Oatmeal Pancakes
Passover Egg Pancakes
Sweet Crêpes

Ordinarily, pancakes are not sweet. I made sweet pancake recipes in order to try to encourage eating them without syrup, and serving them instead with cottage cheese, soft or hard cheese, or yogurt. Also, the sweetened pancakes make more appealing snack items as cold leftovers than do unsweetened pancakes.

DIABETICS AND CHOLESTEROL WATCHERS

It is preferable for you not to eat fritters, as they are extremely high in partly saturated fat (see comments on doughnuts in introduction to Breads, page 99).

FRYING TIPS FOR PANCAKES

Heat a nonstick griddle or skillet; remove from heat and add 1 tsp. butter or oil, tilting pan in order to spread the fat evenly. Return pan to heat; drop batter by spoonfuls onto the pan. When top of pancake is set and begins to bubble, and the cakes move easily with a pancake turner, turn, and lightly brown the other side (second browning typically takes about a minute). When cooked, place pancakes on paper towels in a covered dish in the oven at 250° F in order to keep them warm. Repeat greasing procedure for next batch.

Apple Fritters or Pancakes

12 fritters or pancakes: each 110 cal., ½ fruit, ⅔ bread, ¼ meat, 1–4 fat*

Combine in a medium bowl

¾ cup whole-wheat flour	**1 tsp. cinnamon**
¼ cup soy flour	**Pinch of cloves**
2 tsps. dry yeast	

Set aside. Combine

½ cup thawed,	**2 T oil**
unsweetened apple-juice	**⅔ cup boiling water**
concentrate	

Allow liquid to cool to about 120° F (warmer than lukewarm). Stir into the flour mixture. Set aside in a warm place for about 1 hour. When you are ready to make the fritters, heat deep oil to 375° F. While oil is heating, peel, core and grate

2 large apples

Stir into batter. Beat until foamy

3 eggs

Fold beaten eggs into batter. Deep-fry in oil 1 tablespoon at a time, or pan-fry pancake style. Serve with cheese or cottage cheese.

Banana Fritters

10 servings: each 212 cal.,† 2 fruit, 1 bread, 1 meat, 3–5 fat

Combine and set aside

1 cup whole-wheat flour	**¼ tsp. allspice**
1 cup soy flour	**1/16 tsp. cloves**

Place oil ¼ inch deep in skillet on medium-high heat. Beat together

2 eggs	**½ cup milk**
⅔ cup thawed,	**2 T oil**
unsweetened pineapple-	
juice concentrate	

Stir wet ingredients into dry ingredients. Slice crosswise into ½-inch slices

6 bananas

Dip banana slices into batter and fry on both sides until golden brown. Serve plain or with cottage cheese.

*Lower figure is for pancakes; higher for fritters.
†Add 100–200 calories for frying in relatively deep oil.

Blueberry Pancakes

24 pancakes: each 60 cal., ¼ fruit, ⅓ bread, ¼ milk

Combine

1⅔ cups whole-wheat
   flour

⅓ cup soy flour

Beat well

2 eggs

1⅓ cups milk

½ cup thawed,
   unsweetened apple-juice
   concentrate

2 T thawed, unsweetened
   pineapple-juice
   concentrate

1 tsp. grated orange rind

Stir wet ingredients into dry ingredients. Then stir in

1 cup blueberries

Cook on a lightly buttered nonstick griddle. Serve with cottage cheese.

Buttermilk Pancakes

24 pancakes: each 78 cal., ⅓ fruit, ½ bread, ⅓ milk, ½ meat

(These are sweeter with skim milk, since buttermilk has a sour flavor.)

Combine

⅓ cup soy flour

1⅔ cups whole-wheat
   flour

1½ tsps. baking soda

¼ cup nonfat dry milk

Beat well

2¼ cups buttermilk or
   skim milk

2 T melted butter

3 eggs

¾ cup thawed,
   unsweetened apple-juice
   concentrate

½ tsp. grated lemon rind

Add dry ingredients to milk mixture and beat well. Pan-fry. Serve with Apple Syrup, Cheddar cheese, or cottage cheese.

Carob French Toast

6 slices: each 141 cal., ⅓ fruit, 1 bread, ½ meat, ½ fat

(This is an especially tasty way to serve French toast, and a good way to make eggs appealing to children who don't eat them otherwise.)

Beat well

3 large or 4 small eggs   **½ cup milk**
3 T Cara-Coa powder

Soak in the milk mixture

6 slices whole-grain bread

Fry on both sides with ½ tsp. butter or oil per slice for a total per recipe of

1 T butter or oil

Serve plain. Excellent as snacks.

Cinnamon French Toast

6 slices: each 150 cal., ½ fruit, 1 bread, ¼ milk, ⅓ meat, ½ fat

Combine

3 eggs   **unsweetened pineapple-**
⅓ cup milk   **juice concentrate**
2 tsps. cinnamon   **1 T thawed unsweetened**
¼ cup thawed,   **apple-juice concentrate**

Soak

6 slices whole-grain bread

in the egg mixture. Fry in buttered nonstick pan on both sides until brown.

Variation: Substitute 1 tsp. almond extract for cinnamon, and apple-juice concentrate for the pineapple-juice concentrate.

Cottage-Cheese Pancakes

24 pancakes: each 46 cal., ¼ fruit, ⅕ bread, ⅓ milk, ⅕ fat

In a blender, purée

1 cup cottage cheese   **½ cup thawed,**
2 T nonfat dry milk   **unsweetened apple-juice**
1 tsp. grated orange peel **concentrate**
3 eggs

Beat in

¾ cup whole-wheat flour
¼ cup soy flour

Drop batter by spoonfuls on hot buttered nonstick griddle. Fry on both sides until lightly brown. Serve plain or with grated cheese. Excellent as snacks.

Matzoh Brei Pancakes

12 pancakes: each 53 cal., $\frac{1}{6}$ fruit, $\frac{1}{3}$ bread, $\frac{1}{4}$ meat

Break into small pieces
3 whole-wheat matzoth
Cover with hot water and drain immediately. Beat together

3 eggs   **3 T thawed, unsweetened**
1 tsp. cinnamon   **apple-juice concentrate**

Mix liquid with matzoth. Fry in a heated, nonstick skillet, flattening each cake as you go. Fry on both sides until golden brown. Serve with hard cheese or cottage cheese.

Orange Oatmeal Pancakes

20 pancakes: each 73 cal., $\frac{1}{2}$ fruit, $\frac{1}{3}$ bread, $\frac{1}{3}$ meat, $\frac{1}{5}$ fat

Bring to a boil
2 T oil   **$\frac{1}{3}$ cup thawed**
$\frac{1}{3}$ cup thawed,   **unsweetened orange-**
   unsweetened apple-juice   **juice concentrate**
   concentrate   **$\frac{2}{3}$ cup water**
2 tsps. grated orange peel

Stir in
1 cup oats
Remove from heat. Stir into a mixture of

$\frac{1}{3}$ cup soy flour   **$\frac{1}{4}$ tsp. nutmeg**
$\frac{1}{3}$ cup rye or whole-wheat   **$\frac{1}{16}$ tsp. cloves**
   flour

Beat in
4 eggs   **$\frac{1}{2}$ cup milk**

Fry on lightly buttered nonstick griddle until golden brown on both sides. Serve with cottage cheese or Enriched Peanut Butter.

Passover Egg Pancakes

18 pancakes: each 74 cal., ⅓ fruit, ½ bread, ⅓ meat, ⅕ fat

Crumble and grind in blender to make 1½ cups matzoh meal
  6 whole-wheat matzoth
    (3 at a time)
Beat
  6 eggs   **4 tsps. cinnamon**
  ½ cup thawed,   **1 cup water**
    unsweetened apple-juice
    concentrate

Stir into the matzoh meal. Fry pancakes on both sides until brown. Thin batter as needed with extra water. Serve with cottage cheese or applesauce.

Sweet Crêpes

10 crêpes: each 129 cal., 1 fruit, ½ bread, ½ milk, ½ fat

Beat until foamy
  4 eggs   **⅛ tsp. vanilla extract**

Beat in
  ¾ cup whole-wheat flour   **3 T nonfat dry milk**
  ¼ cup soy flour   **1¼ tsps. cornstarch**

Beat until smooth. While beating, gradually add a mixture of
  ¾ cup water   **1 cup thawed,**
  ¾ cup milk   **unsweetened apple-juice**
                                            concentrate

Continue beating until the batter reaches the consistency of heavy cream. Let batter stand 30 minutes before using. Thin with water if the batter becomes too thick. Fry 1 at a time in a nonstick pan about 7 inches in diameter. Serve with a sweet sauce or filling of your choice, or as Crêpes Suzette. (See Frostings, Fillings, Sauces, and Syrups, pages 143–53.)

SAUCES AND SYRUPS

Apple Syrup
Applesauce
Coffee Syrup
Cranberry Sauce
Lemon Syrup
Licorice Syrup
Sweet-'n-Tart Barbecue Sauce
Tomato Barbecue Sauce

The syrups in this section are designed for pancakes, and should be served warm. The best reheating technique for these syrups is to place the container in a pan partly filled with water, and then to bring the water to a boil. For principles of making cornstarch-based syrups, please refer to Frostings, Fillings, Sauces and Syrups in the Desserts section (page 143).

Apple Syrup

1 cup: each T 12 cal., ½ fruit

Stir in a nonstick pan over medium-high heat until thick

**½ cup unsweetened
apple-juice concentrate**

**½ cup water
1 T cornstarch or
arrowroot powder**

Stir in

¼ tsp. vanilla extract

⅛ tsp. almond extract

Remove from heat. Serve warm.

Applesauce

12 servings (1 quart): each 64 cal., 1½ fruit

Bring to a boil

**6 cups peeled, chopped
apples
¾ cup unsweetened
apple-juice concentrate**

**1½ tsp. cinnamon
¾ cup water**

Cover. Reduce heat and simmer for 20 minutes. Purée. Refrigerate.

Coffee Syrup

1 cup: each T 33 cal., ½ fruit

Stir over medium-high heat in a nonstick pan until thick

**1 cup unsweetened apple-
juice concentrate
1 T cornstarch**

**2 tsps. instant
decaffeinated coffee
1 T unsweetened orange-
juice concentrate**

Serve warm.

Cranberry Sauce

10 servings (1 quart): each 90 cal., 2 fruit

Let stand

2 T unsweetened orange-juice concentrate

2 tsps. (1 package) unflavored gelatin

Bring to a boil in a nonstick pan

4 cups (1 1-lb. package) cranberries

1¼ cups unsweetened apple-juice concentrate

Cover. Reduce heat to medium; simmer for 20 minutes. Stir in the gelatin mixture and remove from heat. Refrigerate.

Lemon Syrup

1 cup: each T 17 cal., 1 fruit

Stir over medium-high heat

½ cup unsweetened apple-juice concentrate

½ cup water

2 T lemon juice

1 T cornstarch

When thick, stir in

¼ tsp. almond extract

Remove from heat. Serve warm.

Licorice Syrup

1 cup: each T 17 cal., 1 fruit

Cook until thick

½ cup unsweetened apple-juice concentrate

½ cup water

1 T cornstarch

Stir in

⅛ tsp. vanilla extract
⅛ tsp. almond extract

½ tsp. anise extract

Serve warm.

Sweet-'n-Tart Barbecue Sauce

1½ cups: each T 14 cal., ⅓ fruit

Bring to a boil

2 tsps. cornstarch or arrowroot powder	**2 tsps. instant decaffeinated coffee**
1 T apple-cider vinegar	**½ cup dark raisins**
¼ cup unsweetened orange-juice concentrate	**1 tsp. oil**
	1 T grated lemon peel
1 cup water	**1 clove garlic, crushed**
	½ tsp. ginger
	¼ tsp. cloves

Reduce heat to medium. Stir until thick. Purée. Refrigerate until ready to use.

Tomato Barbecue Sauce

1⅔ cups: each T 22 cal., ½ fruit
(This sauce was considered among the best barbecue sauces that several of the tasters had ever eaten.)

Bring to a boil

1 8-oz. can tomato sauce	**½ tsp. ginger**
1 6-oz. can pineapple-juice concentrate	**½ tsp. cinnamon**
	¼ tsp. cloves
3 T apple-cider vinegar	**1 clove garlic, crushed**
2 tsps. Worcestershire sauce	**1 T oil or margarine**

Stir to blend. Cover and simmer on lowered heat for 5 minutes. Refrigerate until ready to use.

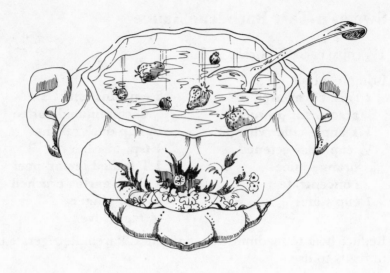

SOUPS

Apricot Soup
Blueberry Soup
Melon-Ball Soup
Peach Soup
Strawberry Soup

Most of these soups are lightly sweetened. They are included in the Main-Meal Sweets section because they can be used either as an appetizer or as part of the main meal, as well as for dessert or snacks (including being frozen into popsicles). The recipes here represent a variety of approaches involving, in order of increasing saturated fat and caloric content, buttermilk, yogurt, cottage cheese, sour cream, and whipping cream. If desired, the soups may also be used as beverages (including the Melon-Ball Soup, if puréed).

GOURMET SERVING SUGGESTIONS

Serve garnished with a dollop of yogurt or sour cream, sprinkled with sliced almonds, with a thin slice of orange or a sprig of fresh mint.

Apricot Soup

8 servings: each 110 cal., 1 fruit, ⅓ milk, ½ meat, ¼ fat

Purée
**2 cups fresh or thawed
apricots
1 cup cottage cheese
⅓ cup unsweetened
apple-juice concentrate**
**⅓ cup unsweetened
pineapple-juice
concentrate
½ tsp. grated orange peel
¹⁄₁₆ tsp. nutmeg**
Pour into a 1½-quart bowl. Beat in
1½ cups plain yogurt

Blueberry Soup

8 servings: each 100 cal., 1 fruit, ¼ milk, ⅔ meat

Purée
**1½ tsps. minced fresh
mint or ½ tsp. dried
mint**
2 cups cottage cheese
Blend in
**2 cups fresh or thawed
blueberries**
**⅓ cup unsweetened pear-
grape concentrate**
Chill before serving.

Melon-Ball Soup

8 servings: each 127 cal., ½ fruit, 1 milk, ⅓ fat

Using the small end of the melon baller, cut out
**2 cups honeydew and/or
cantaloupe balls**
Set aside with any extra melon juice. In blender, purée
**1 cup cottage cheese
1 cup plain yogurt
4 T nonfat dry milk
½ cup freshly squeezed
and strained lemon
juice**
**¼ cup unsweetened
apple-juice concentrate
2 tsps. finely grated lemon
rind**
Stir in melon balls.

Peach Soup

8 servings: each 95 cal., 1½ fruit, ½ milk

Purée
    2 cups fresh or thawed   **⅓ cup thawed,**
      peaches   **unsweetened pineapple-**
    1 cup buttermilk   **juice concentrate**
    ½ tsp. cinnamon   **½ cup unsweetened**
                              apple-juice concentrate

Pour into a 1½-quart bowl. Beat in
    2 cups buttermilk

Strawberry Soup

10 servings: each 156 cal., 2 fruit, ½ veg, 1 fat

Bring to a boil
    3 cups sliced strawberries   **¾ cups unsweetened**
                                    apple-juice concentrate

Lower heat. Simmer for 5 minutes. Stir in a mixture of
    1 T cornstarch   **½ cup unsweetened**
    Juice of 1 lemon   **orange-juice**
    1 cup freshly squeezed   **concentrate**
      orange juice

Stir until thick. Purée. Chill before serving. When ready to serve, beat in
    1 cup sour cream
    ½ cup heavy cream

SECTION 4

Desserts

Cakes
Cheesecakes
Frostings, Fillings, Sauces, and Syrups
Fruit Desserts
Gelatin Molds
Ice Cream, Ice Milk, Sherbets, and Sorbets
Mousses, Crèmes, and Soufflés
Pastries
Puddings and Custards

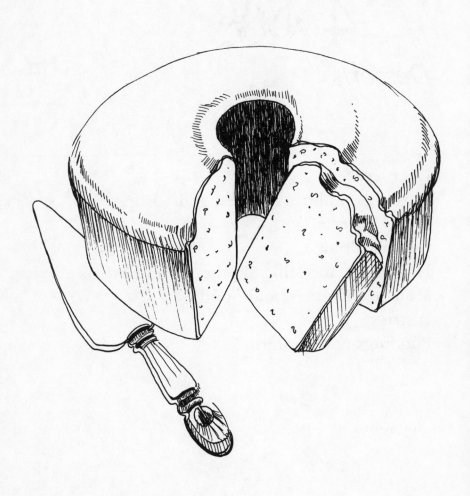

CAKES

Almond Cake

Apple Cake Deluxe

Apple Spice Cake

Banana Cake

Carob Coffee Cake

Carob Cupcakes

Chocolate Soda Cake

Carrot Cake

Crumb Coffee Cake

Devil's Food Cake

Fruit Cake

"Honey" Cake

Lemon Nut Cake

Passover Coffee Cake

Peanut-Butter Coffee Cake

Pineapple Upside-Down Cake

Raisin-Spice Cupcakes

Sponge Cake

Vanilla Cake

Whole-grain flour can vary more than 20 per cent in its ability to absorb moisture, depending upon the type of wheat from which it was milled, processing, and the amount of moisture absorbed or lost during storage. In making whole-grain cakes, the best results are obtained when the batter is fairly wet. Therefore you may need to adjust the liquid proportions in a recipe by a few tablespoonfuls in either direction, depending on how much your particular whole-wheat flour absorbs moisture.

In making whole-grain cakes, sifting is unnecessary because whole-grain flours do not become packed down like white flour (whole-grain flours, incidentally, are lower in calories per cup: see Wheat in Glossary, page 218). The two leavening agents most used in the cakes are eggs and baking soda. Baking soda (see Glossary) is used because it is activated by juice concentrates, and because baking powder (see Glossary) is actually overactivated in the presence of juice concentrates, causing cakes to fall. For best rising, ingredients should be at room temperature at the time of mixing. As quickly as possible after dry and wet ingredients are combined, the cake should go into the preheated oven. Test for doneness by conventional measures: The cake is pulled away from the edges of the pan, and a knife inserted comes out clean. If a cake is still wet inside and yet quite brown on the outside, your oven is probably too hot. If this happens, turn off the oven and allow the cake to stand in the closed oven for about 30 minutes. In this way, the cake can finish baking without burning or becoming too dry. If your cakes do not rise adequately, more than likely you have either overbeaten or underbeaten the eggs, or have let too much time elapse between mixing the wet ingredients with the baking soda, thus losing some of the activation of the soda. Optimum beating time for eggs is between 1 and 2 minutes at high speed of electric mixer. When beating egg whites, one should beat until soft peaks, as opposed to stiff peaks, are formed (in contrast to mousses, in which egg whites are beaten until stiff because they are not cooked afterward).

FOR SNACKS

I suggest leaving cakes unfrosted—they're delicious anyway, lower in calories, and less messy for packing in lunches.

FOR GOURMET SERVING

See comments under Frostings, Fillings, Sauces, and Syrups (page 143), and recommendations in the Gelatin Molds subsection of Desserts (page 157). For deluxe presentation, try slicing both 8-inch round cakes horizontally to make a total of four round layers per recipe. Spread a jam, jelly, or butter between the cut layers, and a pudding or filling between the two uncut surfaces. Serve slices with dollops of whipped cream frosting, chocolate syrup, or ice cream and sliced almonds or chopped cashews.

Cholesterol Watchers

You may eliminate all but one egg yolk per recipe without much loss of richness. If you eliminate all egg yolks, add an extra egg white to the recipe.

Almond Cake

16 servings: each 167 cal., 1 fruit, 1 bread, ½ meat, ½ fat

Grind finely
1 cup blanched almonds
Preheat oven to 350° F. Butter a 9-inch tube pan, and line the bottom with buttered waxed paper, buttered side up. Combine and set aside

2 egg yolks
¼ cup unsweetened pineapple-juice concentrate

¼ cup unsweetened apple-juice concentrate
½ tsp. almond extract

Beat until soft peaks form
6 egg whites

½ tsp. cream of tartar

Beat the yolk-juice mixture into
3 cups date flour

1 tsp. baking soda

Fold in the beaten egg whites. Turn batter into prepared pan. Bake for 1 hour at 350° F.

Apple Cake Deluxe

36 servings: each 163 cal., 1 fruit, ½ bread, 1 meat, 3½ fat

Combine
3 cups chopped apples (peeling optional)
1 cup raisins

1 cup shredded unsweetened coconut
1 cup chopped walnuts

Set aside. Preheat oven to 325° F. Butter a 9 × 13-inch cake pan. Combine
2 cups whole-wheat flour
1 cup soy flour

1½ tsps. baking soda
1 tsp. cinnamon

Stir in
1 cup oil
6 eggs

1½ cups unsweetened apple-juice concentrate

Beat at high speed with electric mixer for 1 minute. Stir in the fruit and nut mixture. Turn into the cake pan. Bake for 1 hour at 325° F.

Apple Spice Cake

16 servings: each 183 cal., 1 fruit, 1 bread, ½ meat, 1 fat

Grate enough apple to make
1½ cups grated apple
Set aside. Preheat oven to 350° F. Butter two 8-inch layer-cake pans. Combine

3 cups date flour	**½ tsp. cloves**
1 tsp. baking soda	**½ tsp. nutmeg**
2 tsps. cinnamon	

Stir in

½ cup oil	**½ cup milk**
4 eggs	

Beat at high speed with electric mixer for 1 minute. Pour into the layer-cake pan. Bake for 35 minutes at 350° F.

Banana Cake

16 servings: each 218 cal., 1½ fruit, 1 bread, ½ meat, 1 fat

Soak overnight

1 cup milk	**1 cup raisins**

Preheat oven to 350° F. Butter two 8-inch cake pans.
Purée

1 cup mashed banana	**¼ tsp. nutmeg**
½ cup oil	**1 tsp. vanilla extract**

Combine the milk, raisins, and banana purée with

3 cups date flour	**4 eggs**
1 tsp. baking soda	

Beat for 1 minute at high speed with electric mixer. Pour into the prepared cake pans. Bake for 40 minutes at 350° F.

Carob Coffee Cake

16 servings: each 108 cal., 1 bread, ⅓ meat, ½ fat

Pan-roast in preheated skillet over medium heat

1 cup whole-wheat flour	**¼ cup soy flour**

Stir at 30-second intervals and pack the flour down between stirrings. Set aside. Preheat oven to 350° F. Butter two 8-inch cake pans. Purée

½ cup mashed banana   1 cup Cara-Coa Powder
1 cup milk

Combine with the roasted flour along with

2 tsps. baking powder   ¼ cup oil
2 eggs

Beat at high speed for 1 minute. Pour into the prepared cake pans. Bake at 350° F for 15–18 minutes.

Carob Cupcakes

3 dozen: each 113 cal., ⅔ fruit, ⅔ bread, ⅓ meat, ½ fat

Boil for 5 minutes in a 2-quart saucepan

4 cups prune juice   ½ cup margarine
1 cup raisins

Stir in

1½ cups whole-wheat   1 cup carob flour (1⅓
    flour   cups Cara-Coa Powder)
¼ cup soy flour   ½ tsp. nutmeg

Remove from heat. Preheat oven to 350° F. Prepare muffin tins with paper muffin cups or by greasing individual muffin holders. Beat into the flour mixture

¼ cup evaporated milk   4 eggs
1 cup nonfat dry milk   1 tsp. baking soda

Pour into the prepared muffin containers. Bake at 350° F for 25 minutes.

Chocolate Soda Cake

16 servings: each 137 cal., 1 fruit, 1 bread

Preheat oven to 350° F.
Mix

2 cups date flour   5 T unsweetened cocoa
1 tsp. baking soda   powder

Stir in

1 cup thawed,   1 T vanilla extract
    unsweetened pear-grape
    concentrate

Turn into a buttered 8 × 8-inch cake pan. Bake at 350° F until done, about 25 minutes.

Carrot Cake

20 servings: each 200 cal., ½ fruit, 1 bread, ¼ veg, 2 fat

Soak overnight
  1 cup raisins   **1 cup water**
Prepare
  ¾ cup chopped nuts   **1 cup grated carrots**
Preheat oven to 325° F. Butter a 5–6-cup ring mold or 8-inch square cake pan. Blend
  3 cups date flour   **1 tsp. baking soda**
  1 tsp. cinnamon   **½ cup softened butter or**
  ½ tsp. nutmeg   **margarine**
  ¼ tsp. cloves
Add
  ¼ cup thawed,   **¼ cup thawed,**
    unsweetened orange-   **unsweetened apple-juice**
    juice concentrate   **concentrate**
                                                   4 eggs
Add the raisins and water. Beat the mixture for 1 minute at high speed. Stir in the nuts and carrots. Turn into the prepared pan. Bake for 1 hour at 325° F if using the ring mold; bake for 45 minutes if using the 8 × 8-inch cake pan.

Crumb Coffee Cake

16 servings: each 160 cal., 1 fruit, ½ bread, ⅓ meat, 1½ fat

Blend and set aside
  ⅓ cup date flour   **2 T butter**
Preheat oven to 350° F. Butter an 8 × 8-inch cake pan. Blend until a fine-crumb consistency
  2 cups date flour   **½ cup butter or**
  ¾ tsp. baking soda   **margarine**
Beat in
  3 egg yolks   **¼ cup evaporated milk**
  ½ cup buttermilk
Beat until soft peaks form
  3 egg whites   **½ tsp. cream of tartar**
Fold egg whites into batter. Turn batter into the prepared cake pan. Sprinkle crumb mixture over top. Bake 35–40 minutes at 350° F.

Devil's Food Cake

16 servings: each 208 cal., 1½ fruit, 1 bread, ¼ meat, 2 fat

Bring to a boil in a nonstick pan

1¼ cups unsweetened pear-grape concentrate

½ cup chopped dates (12 medium dates)

Stir in until dissolved

½ cup unsweetened cocoa powder

Stir in

1 T vanilla extract

Purée. Preheat oven to 350° F. Butter two 8-inch layer-cake pans. Combine

3 cups date flour

1 tsp. baking soda

Beat in the cooled chocolate mixture along with

5 eggs

½ cup oil

1 tsp. cinnamon

Pour into prepared cake pans. Bake at 350° F. for 30 minutes.

Fruit Cake

20 servings: each 195 cal., 1½ fruit, 1 bread, 2 fat

Soak overnight

1 cup currants or chopped raisins

1 cup chopped dates (24 medium dates)

1 cup chopped dried apricots

¾ cup unsweetened pineapple-juice concentrate

½ cup unsweetened pear-grape concentrate

Preheat oven to 350° F. Line the bottom of a 9-inch tube pan with buttered waxed paper (buttered surface up). Blend

1½ cups date flour

1 tsp. baking soda

¾ cup margarine or butter

Beat until foamy

3 eggs

Stir into flour mixture along with the juice-fruit mixture. Transfer to prepared pan. Bake about 1 hour at 350° F. Let stand until outside of pan is cool, then invert cake onto platter.

Alternative: In soaking the dried fruit, include 3 T dark rum.

"Honey" Cake

20 servings: each 208 cal., 2 fruit, 1 bread, 1 meat, ½ fat

Boil

½ cup water	1 cup unsweetened apple-
1 cup raisins	juice concentrate

Stir in to dissolve

**1 tsp. instant
  decaffeinated coffee**

Cool to room temperature. Preheat oven to 325° F. Butter a 9-inch tube pan. Combine

4 cups date flour	1 tsp. ginger
½ cup chopped nuts	¼ tsp. mace
1 tsp. baking soda	¼ tsp. cloves
2 tsps. cinnamon	

Add the coffee mixture along with

4 eggs	¼ cup oil

Beat at high speed for 1 minute. Stir in the nuts. Pour into the prepared tube pan. Bake at 325° F for 1 hour, 10 minutes. Cover with aluminum foil at 30 minutes in order to prevent over-browning.

Lemon Nut Cake

16 servings: each 203 cal., 1 fruit, 1 bread, ½ meat, 2 fat

Preheat oven to 350° F. Butter two 8-inch layer-cake pans. Combine

1 cup whole-wheat flour	1 tsp. baking soda
½ cup soy flour	½ cup softened margarine
½ cup brown rice flour or	1 cup chopped walnuts
whole-wheat flour	

Add to the flour mixture

2 eggs	
1½ cups unsweetened	2 tsps. grated lemon rind
apple-juice concentrate	1 tsp. almond extract

Beat for 1 minute at high speed. Pour batter into prepared cake pans. Bake 30 minutes at 350° F.

Passover Coffee Cake

16 servings: each 190 cal., ⅔ fruit, 1 bread, ½ meat, 1½ fat

Bring to a boil

¾ **cup unsweetened apple-juice concentrate**	**1 T unsweetened orange-juice concentrate**
½ **cup margarine**	

Stir in

1 tsp. instant coffee	**2 tsps. cinnamon**

Set aside. Preheat oven to 350° F. Grease an 8 × 8-inch cake pan. Blend and set aside

2 T margarine	⅓ **cup date meal**

When the coffee mixture is cooled, combine with

2 cups date meal	**3 egg yolks**

Beat until soft peaks form

6 egg whites
¼ **tsp. salt**
¼ **tsp. lemon juice**

Beat the batter for 30 seconds, then fold in the egg whites. Transfer batter to the cake pan. Sprinkle with crumb topping. Bake at 350° F for 30 minutes.

Peanut-Butter Coffee Cake

16 servings: each 147 cal., 1 fruit, ½ bread, ½ meat, 1 fat

Preheat oven to 350° F. Butter an 8 × 8-inch cake pan. Blend

½ **cup peanut butter**	¾ **tsp. baking soda**
⅓ **cup margarine**	⅛ **tsp. salt**
2 cups date flour	

Add

2 T unsweetened apple-juice concentrate	**2 eggs**
	½ **tsp. almond extract**

Beat for 1 minute at high speed. Turn into the prepared pan. Bake 30 minutes at 350° F.

Pineapple Upside-Down Cake

24 servings: each 190 cal., 1 fruit, 1 bread, 2 fat

Have on hand

1 20-oz. can unsweetened pineapple rings

2 dozen fresh or frozen dark cherries

Combine the juice from the can of pineapple with

⅓ cup unsweetened pineapple-juice concentrate

4 T cornstarch

Stir over medium-high heat until thick. Set aside. Melt in a 9 × 13-inch cake pan

3 T margarine

Spread evenly over bottom of pan. Place pineapple rings across bottom of pan. Place a cherry in the center of each ring, and scatter cherries between the rings. Spread the thickened juice evenly over the pineapple and cherries. Set aside. Preheat oven to 350° F. Combine

1 cup whole-wheat flour
2 cups date flour
1½ tsps. baking soda

¼ cup nonfat dry milk
¾ cup softened margarine

Add

⅓ cup unsweetened pineapple-juice concentrate

⅔ cup unsweetened apple-juice concentrate
4 eggs

Beat for 1 minute at high speed. Pour the batter over the fruit. Bake at 350° F. for 30 minutes. Invert the cake onto a serving plate immediately upon removal from the oven.

Raisin-Spice Cupcakes

2 dozen: each 142 cal., 1 fruit, ⅔ bread, ⅓ meat, 1 fat

Preheat oven to 350° F. Prepare muffin tins by greasing or with paper muffin cups. Boil for 5 minutes

1½ cups unsweetened apple-juice concentrate

½ cup oil
1 cup raisins

Stir in

1¾ cups whole-wheat flour
¼ cup soy flour

2 tsps. cinnamon
½ tsp. cloves

Remove from heat. Cool to lukewarm

Add

3 eggs

1 cup milk

½ cup nonfat dry milk

1 tsp. baking soda

Beat for 1 minute at high speed. Bake at 350° F for 20–25 minutes.

Sponge Cake

16 servings: each 197 cal., 1½ fruit, ⅔ bread, ½ meat, ⅓ fat

Bring to a boil

2 cups unsweetened apple-juice concentrate

½ cup oil

Stir in

1½ cups whole-wheat flour

½ cup soy flour

Remove from heat. Preheat oven to 350° F. Butter two 8-inch cake pans. Combine and set aside

2 T vanilla extract

6 egg yolks

½ cup milk

1 tsp. baking soda

Beat until soft peaks form

6 egg whites

½ tsp. cream of tartar

Beat the yolk mixture into batter at top speed of mixer for 1 minute. Fold the egg whites into the batter. Pour into the prepared cake pans. Bake at 350° F for 30 minutes.

Vanilla Cake

16 servings: each 188 cal., 1 fruit, 1 bread, ⅓ meat, 1½ fat

Preheat oven to 350° F. Butter two 8-inch cake pans. Blend

3 cups date flour

1 tsp. baking soda

Add

3 eggs

½ cup oil

½ cup evaporated milk

1 T vanilla extract

¼ cup unsweetened apple-juice concentrate

Beat for 1 minute at high speed. Turn into prepared cake pans. Bake at 350° F for 25 minutes.

Variation: Almond Cake: Substitute 1 tsp. almond extract for the vanilla extract.

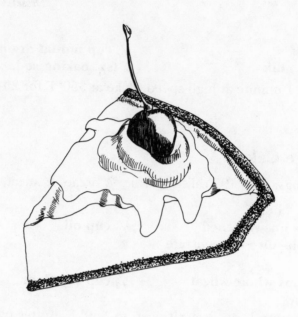

CHEESECAKES

Chocolate Cheesecake, Refrigerator Style
Chocolate-Raspberry Cheesecake, New York Style
Lowfat Cheescake, Refrigerator Style
New York-Style Cheesecake
Pineapple Lowfat Cheesecake, Refrigerator Style
Refrigerator Cheesecake
Toasted Nut Cheesecake

DIABETICS

For high-fat cheesecakes (over 4 fat portions per serving) divide the would-be 12-serving cheesecakes into 20 servings, and the would-be 20-serving cheesecakes into 30 servings in order to keep within the limit of 3–4 fat portions per serving.

GOURMET SERVING SUGGESTIONS

Serve topped with a dessert sauce, syrup, or filling of your choice. Garnish with fresh fruit (cherry, blueberries, strawberries).

Chocolate Cheesecake, Refrigerator Style

12 servings: each 360 cal., 1½ fruit, 1 milk, 6 fat

Prepare in advance, and have cool, a
  Nut Crust (see page 185)
Let stand

¼ cup unsweetened pear-grape concentrate	**2 tsps. (1 package) unflavored gelatin**
1 T vanilla extract	

Bring to a boil

¾ cup unsweetened pear-grape concentrate	**2 oz. unsweetened dark chocolate**
½ cup chopped dates (12 medium dates)	

Stir in the gelatin mixture. Purée in blender. Beat in
  16 oz. cream cheese
Pour into the crust. Chill until firm.

Chocolate-Raspberry Cheesecake, New York Style

20 servings: each 228 cal., 2½ fruit, 1 meat, 3 fat

Have at room temperature

3 8-oz. packages cream cheese	**2 eggs**

Lightly butter a 9-inch spring-form pan. Sprinkle an unbaked recipe of
  Crumb Crust (see page 180)
over bottom of pan. Boil for 5 minutes

1 cup unsweetened pear-grape concentrate	**1 cup packed fresh or thawed raspberries**
3 oz. unsweetened baking chocolate	**1 cup chopped dates (24 medium dates)**

Stir in
  1 T vanilla extract
Purée in blender. Cool to lukewarm. Beat in the eggs and cream cheese. Pour into prepared pan. Bake at 350° F for 45 minutes.

Lowfat Cheesecake, Refrigerator Style

12 servings: each 219 cal., 1½ fruit, ⅓ bread, 1 milk, 2 fat

Prepare in advance a
**Crumb Crust (see page
180)**
Stir occasionally over medium-low heat until clear
**1½ cups unsweetened   4 tsps. (2 packages)
apple-juice concentrate   unflavored gelatin**

Cool to room temperature. Beat together with
**1½ cups yogurt   1½ cups puréed or
1 tsp. grated lemon rind   strained cottage cheese**

Pour into a cooled Crumb Crust. Refrigerate several hours until set. Serve topped by a filling of your choice.

New York-Style Cheesecake

20 servings: each 256 cal., 1⅓ fruit, 1 meat, 4 fat

Bring to a boil
**1 cup unsweetened apple-   ¾ cup chopped dates (18
juice concentrate   medium dates)**

Cover. Boil for 5 minutes. Stir in
1 T vanilla extract
Purée in blender. While puréeing, add in the following order
**8 oz. softened cream   2 eggs
cheese   5 T nonfat dry milk**

Transfer to a large bowl. Beat in
**3 8-oz. packages softened
cream cheese**
Pour into a 9-inch spring-form pan lined with an unbaked Nut Crust (see page 185) or Crumb Crust (see page 180). Bake for 1 hour at 325° F. Allow to cool in oven with the door ajar for 1 hour.

Pineapple Low-Fat Cheesecake, Refrigerator Style

12 servings: each 216 cal., 1 fruit, ½ bread, ¾ milk, 2 fat

Prepare in advance a
  Crumb Crust (see page 180)
Heat to dissolve gelatin (do not boil)
  1 cup crushed pineapple, in its own juice   **½ cup unsweetened pineapple-juice concentrate**
  ¼ cup unsweetened apple-juice concentrate
Cool to room temperature. Purée in blender
  1 cup cottage cheese   **6 T nonfat dry milk**
  1½ cup yogurt
Stir the pineapple sauce into the puréed cottage-cheese mixture. Pour into the prepared crust. Chill until set.

Refrigerator Cheesecake

12 servings: each 327 cal., 1 fruit, ½ bread, ⅘ milk, 4½ fat

Prepare in advance a
  Crumb Crust (see page 180)
Heat to dissolve gelatin
  2 tsps. (1 package) unflavored gelatin   **2 T thawed, unsweetened pineapple-juice concentrate**
  ¾ cup thawed, unsweetened apple-juice concentrate   **1 tsp. grated lemon rind**

Stir in
  2 tsps. vanilla extract
Remove from heat. Cool to room temperature. Beat in
  2 8-oz. packages softened cream cheese
Pour into the prepared crust. Chill until set. Serve with a sauce or filling of your choice.

Toasted Nut Cheesecake

20 servings: each 309 cal., 1⅓ fruit, ½ milk, ⅓ meat, 4½ fat

Have at room temperature
2 lbs. cream cheese　　　　　　　**4 eggs**

Toast at 300° F. for ½ hour
**1½ cups blanched
  almonds or raw cashews**
Leave oven on after removing nuts. When nuts are done, grind them fine in blender. Set aside. Bring to a boil in a nonstick pan
1 cup unsweetened apple-　　　**2 T butter**
  juice concentrate　　　　　**1¼ cups dates**

Cover. Reduce heat to medium and simmer for 5 minutes. Stir in
1 T vanilla extract
Purée in blender.

　Beat the cream cheese and eggs together in a large bowl with an electric mixer on low speed. Gradually beat in the puréed fruit mixture. As the ingredients blend, increase the speed to high. Beat until blended and smooth. Beat in the ground roasted nuts. Butter a 9-inch spring-form pan. Sprinkle the inside with
⅓ cup date flour
Shape the crumbs around the bottom and sides until coated. Shake out excess, and set aside. Pour in the cheesecake batter. Sprinkle top with remaining date flour. Bake cheesecake for 2 hours at 300° F. Let stand in oven to cool for 1 hour.

FROSTINGS, FILLINGS, SAUCES, AND SYRUPS

Carob Syrup
Chantilly Cream
Cherry Filling
Cherry Sauce
Chocolate Cream-Cheese Frosting
Chocolate Sauce or Glaze
Chocolate Syrup
Coconut Glaze
Cream-Cheese Frosting
Crêpes Suzette Filling
Fig Cookie Filling
Fudge Frosting
Hot Buttered Rum Sauce
Maple Syrup
Meringue Topping
Milk Chocolate Frosting
Orange Frosting
Orange Glaze
Pineapple Filling
Strawberry Hamantaschen Filling
Vanilla Egg Icing
Vanilla Glaze
Whipped Cream Topping

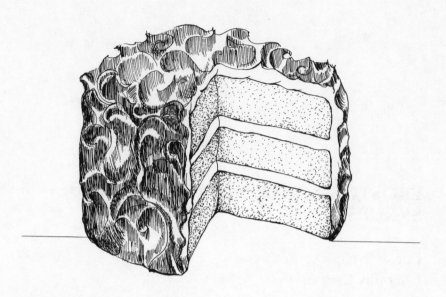

FROSTINGS

are obviously most appropriate for cakes, cupcakes, doughnuts, and cookies. Frostings may be thickened by adding more non-fat dry milk, and thinned by adding more milk or water. Frostings and whipped creams may be used with a cake-decorating kit. When decorating cakes and cupcakes, consider using such decorators as raisins, currants, blueberry halves, strawberry slivers, and nut pieces.

GLAZES

should be used when cool. When the cake is done and still warm, pour on the glaze, pricking the cake amply in order to help the glaze seep in. Place cake in preheated oven at 350° F for 10 to 15 minutes, until glaze is hot and glossy.

DIETERS AND DIABETICS

Each recipe yields 1 to 1½ cups, so you may expect to use 1 to 1½ T icing per slice of two-layer cake (based on the usual 16 slices per two-layer cake). In some cases, frosting a cake will take your serving over the limit of 2 fruit portions or 4 fat portions at a sitting—so proceed with caution in frosting your cakes.

Carob Syrup

1½ cups: each T 33 cal., ½ fruit, ⅙ meat

Heat to near boiling
  1 cup evaporated milk
Stir in
  **1 cup fine carob powder
    (Cara-Coa Powder is a
    reliable brand.)**
When well blended, transfer to a glass jar. Refrigerate.

Chantilly Cream

1½ cups: each T 54 cal., ⅓ fruit, 1 fat

Soak overnight
  **⅓ cup finely chopped   1 cup whipping cream
    golden raisins**

Strain to squeeze moisture from raisins. Recombine raisins with cream. Beat cream plus raisins until stiff peaks form. While continuing to beat, add
  **3 T thawed, unsweetened
    orange-juice
    concentrate**
Stop beating. Fold in
  ½ cup sour cream
Beat again until mixture is thick and holds its shape.
Refrigerate until ready to use.

Cherry Filling

1½ cups: each T 20 cal., ½ fruit

Cook over medium-high heat, stirring until thick
  **2 T cornstarch   2 T thawed, unsweetened
  1½ cups pitted dark   orange-juice concentrate
    cherries   6 T thawed, unsweetened
                              pear-grape concentrate**

Cool to room temperature or chill before using. For a sweeter filling, see the Strawberry Cookie Filling.

Variations: Blueberry Filling: Substitute blueberries for cherries.

Strawberry Filling: Substitute strawberries for cherries; apple-juice concentrate for pear-grape concentrate.

Cherry Sauce

2 cups: each ¼ cup 15 cal., ½ fruit

Purée in blender or food processor

1 cup frozen dark cherries (about 30 cherries)
⅓ cup thawed, unsweetened pear-grape concentrate
¼ cup thawed, unsweetened apple-juice concentrate

Combine in a saucepan with

5 tsps. cornstarch
½ cup water
12 diced dark cherries

Cook until thick, stirring constantly. Remove from heat. Stir in

¼ tsp. almond extract

Chill before serving or serve at room temperature.

Chocolate Cream-Cheese Frosting

1½ cups: each T 60 cal., ½ fruit, 1 fat

Bring to a boil in a nonstick pan

1 oz. unsweetened chocolate
3 T thawed, unsweetened pear-grape concentrate
3 T water
½ cup chopped dates (12 medium dates)
1 T margarine

Purée in blender. When smooth and lukewarm, beat in

8 oz. soft cream cheese

Chocolate Sauce or Glaze

1½ cups: each T 20 cal., ½ fruit

Stir in nonstick pan over medium-high heat until thick

1 T cornstarch
¾ cup water
¾ cup unsweetened pear-grape concentrate

Remove from heat. Stir in

⅓ cup unsweetened cocoa powder

Return to heat for another minute, stirring until smooth. Stir in

2 tsps. vanilla extract

Remove from heat. Serve warm or at room temperature. Store in refrigerator.

Chocolate Syrup

1½ cups: each T 35 cal., 1 fruit

Bring to a boil
  **1½ cups (1 12-oz. can)
    pear-grape concentrate**
Stir in
  **½ cup unsweetened cocoa
    powder**
When cocoa is dissolved, stir in
  1 T vanilla extract
Pour into a clean glass container. Refrigerate.

Coconut Glaze

1½ cups: each T 18 cal., ⅓ fruit, ⅒ fat

Soak overnight
  **½ cup grated
    unsweetened coconut**
  **⅓ cup unsweetened
    apple-juice concentrate**

**2 T chopped dates (3
  medium dates)**

When ready to cook, combine in a nonstick pan with
  2 T cornstarch   **¾ cup water**

Stir over high heat until thick. Remove from heat. Purée in blender. Cool to room temperature before using.

Cream-Cheese Frosting

1½ cups: each T 51 cal., ⅓ fruit, 1 fat

Bring to a boil
  **½ cup chopped dates (12
    medium dates)**
  **1 T thawed, unsweetened
    apple-juice concentrate**

**3 T water
1 T margarine**

Cover. Simmer for 5 minutes. Purée in blender. When luke-warm, beat in
  **8 oz. softened cream
    cheese**
If frosting is too runny for immediate use, chill slightly before spreading.

Crêpes Suzette Filling

1 cup: each T 68 cal., ½ fruit, ⅔ fat

Bring to a boil in a nonstick pan

**½ cup butter or
   margarine
1 T grated orange peel
⅓ cup date pieces (about
   8 medium dates,
   chopped)**

**2 T thawed, unsweetened
   apple-juice concentrate
2 T thawed, unsweetened
   orange-juice
   concentrate**

Cover and boil for 5 minutes. Purée. Refrigerate. When ready to serve, spead mixture on cooked crêpes, roll up, and place on heated serving dish. Keep warm in oven at 200° F. Place in saucepan over low heat and warm

¼ cup brandy

When ready to eat, pour warm brandy over crêpes, ignite, and serve flaming.

Fig Cookie Filling

2½ cups: each T 27 cal., ½ fruit

Bring to a boil

**1½ cups chopped figs
1 cup dark raisins
¼ cup water**

**¼ cup thawed,
   unsweetened apple-juice
   concentrate**

Cover. Boil for 5 minutes. Refrigerate.

Variation: Apricot: Substitute dried apricots for figs and golden raisins for dark raisins.

Fudge Frosting

1¼ cups: each T 64 cal., 1 fruit, ⅔ fat

Bring to a boil

**3 T butter or margarine
2 oz. unsweetened baking
   chocolate**

**1 cup date pieces (24
   medium dates)
6 T thawed, unsweetened
   pear-grape concentrate**

Reduce heat to medium low. Simmer for 5 minutes. Stir in

1 T vanilla extract

Remove from heat. Purée. Use warm or at room temperature.

Hot Buttered Rum Sauce

1 cup: each T 40 cal., ½ fruit, ½ fat

Cook until thick
½ cup thawed,   **1 T cornstarch**
unsweetened apple-juice
concentrate
Stir into hot sauce
½ cup warm Half-and-   **2 T butter**
Half
When sauce is well blended, remove from heat and stir in
½ tsp. vanilla extract   **1 T rum**
Keep warm to serve.

Maple Syrup

1½ cups: each T 40 cal., ½ fruit, ½ fat

Stir over medium-high heat until thick
½ cup thawed,   **2 T blackstrap molasses**
unsweetened apple-juice **½ cup water**
concentrate   **2 T cornstarch**
Stir in
2 tsps. vanilla extract
Cool to room temperature. Beat in
½ cup evaporated milk

Meringue Topping (for Lemon Meringue Pie)

About 5 cups: 275 cal., 2 fruit, 2 milk

Stir over medium-high heat until thick
⅓ cup thawed,   **1 tsp. cornstarch**
unsweetened apple-juice
concentrate
Stir in
¼ tsp. vanilla extract
Remove from heat. Cool to room temperature. Beat until foamy
5 egg whites
Sprinkle with
½ tsp. cream of tartar

Continue beating until stiff. Gradually add cooled sauce to egg whites, beating continually. Spread meringue over pie or custard. Bake at 400° F for 8 minutes. Turn oven off, and let stand in oven for 30 minutes. Open oven door slightly, and let stand another 15 minutes in oven. (Leaving the meringue in the oven while cooling prevents collapsing.)

Variation: Pineapple Meringue: Use 4 T unsweetened pineapple-juice concentrate and 2 T unsweetened apple-juice concentrate; eliminate vanilla extract.

Milk Chocolate Frosting

1½ cups: each T 58 cal., ⅔ fruit, ½ fat

Bring to a boil
**¼ cup unsweetened pear-
    grape concentrate**   **6 T butter**
½ cup water   **1 cup chopped dates (24
                                medium dates)**
Cover. Let boil 5 minutes. Add
**2 oz. unsweetened
    chocolate**
Cover again until chocolate is melted. Stir in
2 tsps. vanilla extract
Remove from heat. Purée in blender. Let cool to lukewarm. Gradually add (while blending)
¾ cup nonfat dry milk
Spread at room temperature.

Orange Frosting

1 cup: each T 83 cal., ½ fruit, ⅓ milk, 1 fat

Bring to a boil in a nonstick pan
6 T butter   **¼ cup thawed,
**⅓ cup date pieces (8   unsweetened orange-
    medium dates, chopped   juice concentrate**
    or golden raisins**   **2 tsps. grated orange rind**
Cover. Let boil 5 minutes. Purée in blender. When cooled to lukewarm, blend in
1 cup nonfat dry milk
Spread at room temperature.

Variation: Lemon Frosting: Substitute apple-juice concentrate for orange-juice concentrate, and lemon rind for orange rind.

Orange Glaze

1½ cups: each T 15 cal., ⅓ fruit

Stir in a nonstick pan over medium-high heat until thick

6 T unsweetened orange-juice concentrate
2 T unsweetened apple-juice concentrate

1 cup water
3 T cornstarch

Cool to room temperature or chill slightly before using.

Variation: Pineapple Glaze: Substitute unsweetened pineapple-juice concentrate for orange concentrate.

Pineapple Filling

2 cups: each T 15 cal., ½ fruit

Stir in a saucepan over medium-high heat until thick

2 T cornstarch
2 T unsweetened pineapple-juice concentrate

1 20-oz. can of unsweetened crushed pineapple*

Cool to room temperature or chill before using.

Strawberry Hamantaschen Filling (Cookie Filling)

3 cups: each T 21 cal., ½ fruit

Bring to a boil

2 cups chopped strawberries
1½ cups golden raisins

⅓ cup unsweetened apple-juice concentrate
1 tsp. margarine

Cover and boil for 10 minutes. Mash. Refrigerate until ready to use.

Variation: Cherry Filling: Substitute dark cherries for strawberries; chopped dates (36 medium dates) for raisins, and unsweetened pear-grape concentrate for apple-juice concentrate.

*1 20-oz. can contains 1¼ cups pulp and 1 cup juice.

Vanilla Egg Icing

2 cups: each T 38 cal., ½ fruit, 1 fat

Bring to a boil in a nonstick pan
6 T butter or margarine   **2 T thawed, unsweetened**
1 cup golden raisins   **apple-juice concentrate**
⅔ cup water
1 T thawed, unsweetened
  pineapple-juice
  concentrate

Cover. Boil for 5 minutes. Purée in blender. Beat separately until frothy
1 egg
Blend the partly beaten egg into the hot mixture. Transfer mixture into nonstick pan. Cook for 7 minutes over medium-low heat, stirring frequently. Stir in
1 T vanilla extract
Stir for 1 more minute. Remove from heat and purée again. Cook until thick.

Variation: Almond Egg Icing: Substitute 1 tsp. almond extract for the vanilla extract.

Vanilla Glaze

1 cup: each T 17 cal., ½ fruit

Soak overnight
1 cup raisins or dates   **1½ cups water**
Squeeze liquid out of soaked fruit. Set fruit aside.* Combine liquid with
2 T cornstarch
Stir over medium heat in nonstick pan until thick. Remove from heat and stir in
1 tsp. vanilla extract
Cool to room temperature before using.

*Dried fruit purée may be used in cookies and candies.

Whipped Cream Topping

2 cups: each T 35 cal., ⅕ fruit, ½ fat

Soak the following two mixtures separately for 24 hours (stir
once after 12 hours)

⅓ **cup well-chopped date**   **1 cup whipping cream**
   pieces (8 dates)

and

¼ **cup chopped dates (6**   ¼ **cup milk**
   dates)

Using a strainer, squeeze out moisture from dates and cream.
Keep liquids separate. Beat the cream until stiff. Beat in

¼ **cup noninstant nonfat**
   dry milk

Beat in sweetened milk.

Alternative: Use only the dates and whipping cream and beat
the fruit in along with the cream.

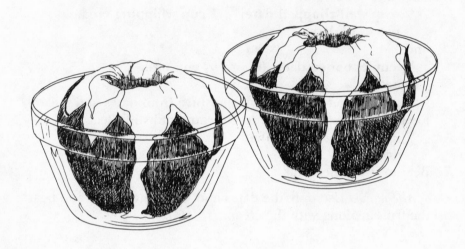

FRUIT DESSERTS

Baked Apples
Baked Pears
Strawberry-Rhubarb Compote
Strawberries Romanoff

DIABETICS

Please take one-half servings of the baked apples at a given sitting.

GOURMET SERVING SUGGESTIONS

Serve Baked Apples with Whipped Cream Topping; Baked Pears with Hot Buttered Rum Sauce or Rum Raisin Ice Cream; Strawberry-Rhubarb Compote over vanilla or chocolate ice cream, topped by Whipped Cream Topping.

Baked Apples

6 servings: each 196 cal., 4 fruit, ⅓ bread, ½ fat*

Remove top half of each, and core
6 large apples
(Make the cavities of ample size.) Chop the apple tops together
with
6 T currants or raisins	**½ tsp. nutmeg**
1 tsp. cinnamon	

Pack some of the mixture into each cavity. Place filled apples,
open side up, in 2-quart rectangular baking dish. Stir together

⅓ cup thawed,   **1 tsp. almond extract**
   unsweetened apple-juice
   concentrate

Pour 1 tsp. of this mixture into each filled cavity. Pour remainder of the mixture plus
½ cup boiling water
into baking dish. Dot each apple with
½ tsp. butter (total for
   recipe of 1 T)
Bake at 400° F 40 to 60 minutes or until tender, basting several
times with the juices. Serve hot or cold.

Baked Pears

8 servings: each 98 cal., 1 fruit, ½ fat

Halve and core
4 large pears
Combine
1 T melted butter	**¼ cup chopped, blanched**
¼ tsp. almond extract	**almonds**

Fill pear cavities with almond mixture. Place in baking dish. Stir
together

¼ cup thawed,   **½ cup water**
   unsweetened apple-juice   **1 tsp. rum**
   concentrate

Distribute the liquid evenly among the pears, pouring it over
each cavity. Bake at 350° F for 30 minutes. Serve hot or cold.

*For 12 servings, follow halving procedure of Baked Pears.

Strawberry-Rhubarb Compote

8 servings: each 84 cal., ⅔ fruit

Combine in a large nonstick pan

    2 cups strawberries
    2 cups sliced rhubarb
    (fresh or frozen)

**1 cup thawed,
unsweetened apple-juice
concentrate**

Sprinkle with

    2 T quick-cooking tapioca

Bring to a boil, stirring occasionally; cover, reduce heat, and simmer for 10 minutes. Serve chilled.

Strawberries Romanoff

8 servings: each 97 cal., 1½ fruit, ⅕ meat, ½ fat*

Wash, dry, stem, and halve

    **1½ lbs. (about 5 cups)
    strawberries**

Place strawberries in large shallow bowl and set aside. Bring to a boil a mixture of

    1 tsp. grated orange rind
    1 tsp. oil
    **6 T thawed, unsweetened
    apple-juice concentrate**

**3 T thawed, unsweetened
orange-juice
concentrate**

Pour hot sauce over strawberries. Refrigerate 3–4 hours, spooning sauce over berries two to four times. To serve, divide berries among 6 or 8 sherbet or balloon wine glasses. Serve with Chantilly Cream mixture (see page 145). Spoon cream over berries and sprinkle each serving with

    **2 tsps. sliced, blanched
    almonds (total amount
    about ⅓ cup)**

*Add in the values for amount of Chantilly Cream used per serving.

GELATIN MOLDS

Apple "Grabbies"
Grape Gel-o
Lemon Chiffon Mold
Orange Gel-o
Pineapple Snow
Strawberry Gelatin
Very Berry Gelatin Pudding

The plain fruit gelatin molds are not as transparent as the commercial varieties, and they are slightly thicker in texture. Gelatin molds, particularly the Apple "Grabbies," are a food which
is well-suited to toddlers, not only because the texture is easy
for them to handle, but also because the amount of juice can be
reduced considerably below the levels called for in the recipes,
and yet still be very appealing to youngsters who have not yet
developed strong expectations of sweetness.

GOURMET SERVING SUGGESTIONS

Different gelatin mold recipes may be combined in alternating
fashion in order to obtain rainbow or parfait effects. Chill one
layer until set, keeping the remainder of the recipe(s) at room
temperature; then add another layer and chill until set, and so
forth. Nuts or whipped cream may be spread between layers,
and a filling of your choice mixed in with any partially set layer.
Whipped cream may also be folded into any partially set layer,
if more gelatin is used, as in the Pineapple Snow recipe.

One-half recipe of a gelatin mold may be used to "frost" a
cake. Remove cakes from pans while still warm, and clean and
lightly butter pans; return cakes to pans, prick generously while
pouring the gelatin mixture (not set) over them. Chill until gelatin is set. Unmold, and serve with Whipped Cream Topping.

Apple "Grabbies"

24 servings: each 15 cal., ⅓ fruit

(Messy, but grab-able. A good finger food for infants and young toddlers.)

Place in nonstick pan
 **¾ cup thawed,
  unsweetened apple-juice
  concentrate**
Sprinkle over surface
 **8 tsps. (4 packages)
  unflavored gelatin**
Set over medium-low heat until gelatin begins to dissolve, about 10 minutes. Stir in
 2¼ cups warm water

Remove from heat. Stir and pour into a lightly buttered bread-loaf pan. Refrigerate until set. Cut into squares about 1 × 1 inch.

Variation: Grape "Grabbies": Substitute unsweetened pear-grape concentrate for apple-juice concentrate.

Grape Gel-o

6 servings: each 65 cal., 1½ fruit

Sprinkle
 2 tsps. unflavored gelatin
over surface of
 **¼ cup thawed,
  unsweetened pear-grape
  concentrate**
Let stand 3 minutes. Stir in a boiling mixture of
 **1½ cups water
 ½ cup unsweetened pear-
  grape concentrate**
Pour into bowl or mold. Chill until firm.

Variation: Apple Gel-o: Substitute unsweetened apple-juice concentrate for pear-grape concentrate.

Lemon Chiffon Mold

12 servings: each 96 cal., 1½ fruit, ½ meat
Place in nonstick pan
   1 cup thawed,
      unsweetened apple-juice
      concentrate
Sprinkle with
   3 tsps. (1½ packages)
      unflavored gelatin
Set over low heat until gelatin is dissolved. Beat gradually into
an already beaten mixture of
   1 T grated lemon rind   **½ cup thawed,**
   6 egg yolks   **unsweetened apple-juice**
                                         concentrate

Return to nonstick pan over medium heat (or place in double
boiler) and stir constantly until thickened. Set aside to cool to
room temperature. When cool, beat until foamy
   6 egg whites
Add
   ½ tsp. cream of tartar   **2 tsps. lemon juice**
Beat until stiff. Fold egg whites into yolk mixture. Pour into
ring mold, and smooth the surface. Chill. Unmold to serve.

Orange Gel-o

10 servings: each 57 cal., 1½ fruit
Sprinkle
   1 tsp. (1½ packages)
      gelatin
over
   3 T thawed, unsweetened
      apple-juice concentrate
Let stand 3 minutes. Add
   2 cups boiling water
Stir to dissolve gelatin. Stir in
   1 cup thawed,
      unsweetened orange-
      juice concentrate
Pour into a wet mold. Chill 4 hours or more.

Variation: Pineapple Gel-o: Substitute pineapple-juice concentrate for orange-juice concentrate.

Pineapple Snow

12 servings: each 137 cal., 1½ fruit, 1½ fat, ⅕ meat

Soak
  4 tsps. (2 packages)
    gelatin in
  4 T cold water
Bring to a boil

2 cups (1 20-oz. can) **crushed pineapple, with** **liquid**	**¾ cup (6 oz.) unsweetened** **pineapple-juice** **concentrate**

Stir in the softened gelatin. Remove from heat immediately. Chill until partially set. Beat until stiff .
  1 cup whipping cream
Beat in
  ½ tsp. vanilla extract
Fold whipped cream into pineapple mixture. Pour into a wet mold, and smooth surface. Chill 4 hours or more.

Strawberry Gelatin

6 servings: each 44 cal., 1 fruit

Sprinkle
  2 tsps. unflavored gelatin
over
  ¼ cup cold water
Let stand 3 minutes. Add

½ cup thawed, **unsweetened apple-juice** **concentrate**	**1 cup boiling water**

Stir to dissolve gelatin. Stir in
  ½ cup puréed
    strawberries (straining
    optional)
Pour into mold or individual cups. Chill until set.

Variations: Raspberry Gelatin: Substitute raspberries for strawberries.

Cherry or Blueberry Gelatin: Substitute ½ cup unsweetened pear-grape concentrate for apple-juice concentrate, and ¾ cup cherries or blueberries for strawberries.

Very Berry Gelatin Pudding

10 servings: each 72 cal., 1⅓ fruit, ¼ milk

Place in nonstick pan

½ cup thawed,
unsweetened pear-grape
concentrate

2 T thawed, unsweetened
orange-juice
concentrate
1 cup water

Sprinkle with
3½ tsps. gelatin
Set over low heat until gelatin dissolves, about 5 minutes. Remove from heat and purée in blender with
2 cups fresh or thawed
frozen blueberries
and/or blackberries
Beat in
½ cup nonfat dry milk
Refrigerate several hours until set.

Variations: Cherry: Substitute pitted dark cherries for blue/blackberries; pineapple-juice concentrate for orange-juice concentrate.

Strawberry: Substitute strawberries for blue/blackberries; apple-juice concentrate for pear-grape concentrate.

Peach: Substitute peaches for blue/blackberries; apple-juice concentrate for pear-grape concentrate; pineapple-juice concentrate for orange-juice concentrate.

ICE CREAM, ICE MILK, SHERBETS, AND SORBETS

Banana Ice Cream
Cherry Ice Milk
Chocolate Ice Milk
Cinnamon-Apple Ice Cream
Grapefruit Ice
Ice Milk Snow
Rum-Raisin Ice Cream
Strawberry Sorbet
Vanilla Ice Cream

GOURMET SERVING SUGGESTIONS

Parfaits and sundaes may be created using fillings and syrups, and Whipped Cream Topping.

TECHNIQUES FOR PREPARATION

The ice creams and ice milks are all written for churn-freezing; sorbets are not, but may be churn-frozen for fluffiest consistency. For lower calories, substitute milk for the whipping-cream and ice-cream recipes; for richer texture, substitute 1 cup whipping cream for 1 cup milk in the ice-milk recipes.

In order to churn-freeze, three basic criteria must be met: (1) The mixture must be thoroughly chilled; (2) the canister should be thoroughly chilled when mixture is added; (3) relatively finely crushed ice should be used for more even, thorough cooling; either table salt or rock salt may be used in order to lower the temperature of the ice for adequate freezing. The following format is the one which I use in making my ice creams.

Prepare mixture(s) in advance; refrigerate overnight. Have ready 8 to 10 pounds of ice and ½ pound of table or rock salt for one batch of ice cream; 10 to 15 pounds of ice and ¾ to 1 pound of table or rock salt for two batches. (These proportions are for a 4-quart ice-cream maker.)

To begin procedure, assemble churn-freeze. Start motor (in order to prevent canister from freezing motionless into the ice/salt mixture which is about to be added); finely crush 4 cups ice; distribute around canister; sprinkle with ¼ cup salt. Repeat layers of ice and salt until ice/salt mixture reaches top of ice-cream canister. Stop motor; pour chilled mixture into the canister; reassemble; start motor; churn for 20 to 30 minutes or until motor stops automatically due to the thickness of the frozen mixture. To do a second batch, follow the same procedure, but save the leftover ice/salt mixture by draining the excess water from the first batch in order to reuse the ice that remains solid.

YIELDS

Expect volumes of churn-frozen desserts to 1¼ to 1½ times the volume of the liquid used in the recipe.

Banana Ice Cream

12 servings: each 160 cal., 1⅓ fruit, ½ milk, 1½ fat

Set over low heat in nonstick pan
  **½ cup thawed,
    unsweetened apple-juice
    concentrate**
Sprinkle with
  1 tsp. gelatin
Heat until gelatin dissolves. Remove from heat and purée in blender with, in the following order,

2½ cups ripe banana	**1 cup milk**
⅔ cup nonfat dry milk	**1 cup whipping cream**

Refrigerate overnight. Churn-freeze.

Cherry Ice Milk

12 servings: each 120 cal., 2 fruit, ⅔ milk

Combine

3 T arrowroot powder or cornstarch	**¼ cup unsweetened pineapple-juice concentrate**

Place in a large skillet over medium-high heat along with

¾ cup unsweetened pear-grape concentrate	**3 cups puréed dark cherries (fresh or thawed)**

Stir until thick. Remove from heat. Cool to room temperature. Beat in

1 cup milk	**1 cup nonfat dry milk**

Chill. Churn-freeze.

Variations: Blueberry Ice Milk: Substitute blueberries for cherries.

Strawberry Ice Milk: Substitute strawberries for cherries; apple-juice concentrate for pear-grape concentrate.

Peach Ice Milk: Substitute peaches for cherries; apple-juice concentrate for pear-grape concentrate, pineapple-juice concentrate for orange-juice concentrate.

Chocolate Ice Milk

12 servings: each 92 cal., 1½ fruit, ½ milk

Heat to boiling in nonstick pan
1 cup thawed,   6 medium dates, chopped
** unsweetened pear-grape**
** concentrate**
Stir in
7 T unsweetened cocoa
** powder**
Purée. While the chocolate sauce is cooling, heat in double boiler
3 cups milk   2 tsps. gelatin
When gelatin is dissolved, remove from heat and let cool to room temperature. When cool, beat milk into chocolate sauce along with
¼ cup nonfat dry milk
Chill thoroughly. Churn-freeze.

Cinnamon-Apple Ice Cream

12 servings: each 150 cal., 1 fruit, ⅓ milk, 2 fat

Let stand
¼ cup thawed,
** unsweetened apple-juice**
** concentrate**
Sprinkled with
2 tsps. gelatin
Bring to boil in nonstick pan
¾ cup thawed,   1 cinnamon stick
** unsweetened apple-juice 2 T butter or margarine**
** concentrate**

Cover. Reduce to medium-low and let simmer for 10 minutes. Bring to a boil again, and stir in gelatin mixture. Immediately remove from heat. Cool to room temperature. Beat in
¼ cup nonfat dry milk   1 cup whipping cream
2 cups milk

Chill thoroughly. Churn-freeze.

Grapefruit Ice

4 servings: each 84 cal., 2 fruit

Let stand 3–5 minutes in mixing bowl
**¼ cup thawed,
 unsweetened apple-juice
 concentrate**
Sprinkled with
2 tsps. unflavored gelatin
Bring to a boil
**½ cup thawed,   1 cup water
 unsweetened grapefruit-
 juice concentrate**
Pour this boiling mixture over the gelatin mixture. Stir to dissolve. Freeze until semisolid, then beat in a large bowl until mushy. Beat until foamy
1 egg white
Sprinkle with
⅛ tsp. cream of tartar
and beat until stiff peaks form. Fold into grapefruit mixture. Freeze in trays or sherbet glasses.

Variations: Orange Ice: Substitute orange-juice concentrate for grapefruit-juice concentrate.

Pineapple Ice: Substitute pineapple-juice concentrate for grapefruit-juice concentrate.

Ice Milk Snow

8 servings: each 74 cal., ½ fruit, ½ milk, ⅕ fat

Beat well in large mixing bowl
2 cups milk   **1 T vanilla extract**
½ cup thawed,   **2 eggs**
 unsweetened apple-juice   **2 T nonfat dry milk**
 concentrate
Add clean, fresh snow until the liquid is absorbed. Stir as little as possible.

Rum-Raisin Ice Cream

12 servings: each 164 cal., 1 fruit, ½ milk, 1½ fat

Bring to a boil in a nonstick pan and stir until thickened
2 T cornstarch   **½ cup thawed,**
¾ cup golden raisins   **unsweetened apple-juice**
                                            concentrate

When thick, stir in
½ cup butter or
   margarine
Remove from heat and purée in blender with
3 T rum
When cooled to room temperature, beat in
6 T nonfat dry milk   3 cups milk
Chill thoroughly. Churn-freeze.

Strawberry Sorbet

6 servings: each 68 cal., 1⅔ fruit

Stir together, then heat in nonstick pan to dissolve
1 tsp. unflavored gelatin   2 T thawed, unsweetened
½ cup thawed,   orange-juice
   unsweetened apple-juice concentrate
   concentrate
Combine with
2 cups strawberry purée
(straining optional)

Freeze until partially frozen. Then beat in a large bowl until mushy. Return to trays or freezer dish, and freeze until firm.

Variations: Raspberry Sorbet: Substitute raspberries for strawberries.

Pineapple Sorbet: Substitute drained fresh or canned pineapple for strawberries; pineapple-juice concentrate for apple-juice concentrate, and apple-juice concentrate for orange-juice concentrate.

Vanilla Ice Cream

12 servings: each 140 cal., 1 fruit, ½ milk, 1½ fat

Set over boiling water in double boiler
   1 cup milk
Sprinkle with
   2 tsps. gelatin
Heat until gelatin dissolves, about 5 minutes. Stir in
   1 T vanilla extract
Remove from heat. Add in the following order
   2½ cups milk   1 cup whipping cream
Beat in
   ¼ cup nonfat dry milk
Combine with
   **1½ cups chopped dates
   (34 medium dates)**
Refrigerate 24 hours, stirring once after about 12 hours. Strain to squeeze moisture out of date purée. (Save purée for other recipes or as sandwich spread.) Churn-freeze the liquid.

MOUSSES, CRÈMES, AND SOUFFLÉS

Chocolate Crème
Chocolate Mousse
Chocolate Soufflé
Lemon Mousse
Orange Soufflé
Raspberry Mousse
Strawberry Soufflé

Mousse and cream sauces are cooked prior to folding in the egg whites and/or whipping cream; soufflés are baked after the egg whites are folded into an uncooked sauce. As used in this section, mousses are lighter than crèmes because mousses contain egg whites.

In order to properly use egg whites, I recommend the following guidelines:

1. Be sure that both the whites and the sauce into which they are folded are at room temperature;

2. Use eggs that are at least one day but no more than one week old;

3. Be sure that beaters are clean and dry when beating egg whites;

4. In order to fold in egg whites, it is helpful to fold, then smooth the surface lightly with the flat edge of a scraper, then repeat folding and smoothing procedure.

GOURMET SERVING SUGGESTIONS

Serve in Butter Tart Crust or Eclair or Cream Puff shells. If in tart crust, top with dollop of Whipped Cream Topping; if in eclair or cream puff shell (Puff Pastry), serve topped by a filling, sauce, or syrup of your choice.

169

Chocolate Crème

8 servings: each 227 cal., 2 fruit, ⅓ meat, 3 fat

Bring to a boil

**2 oz. unsweetened baking
chocolate**

**⅓ cup unsweetened pear-
grape concentrate**

**1 cup dark raisins or
chopped dates (24
medium dates)**

1 T margarine

Cover. Cook for 5 minutes. Stir in

1 T vanilla extract

Purée in blender. Refrigerate until cold. When ready, beat until stiff

1 cup whipping cream

Fold whipped cream into chocolate mixture. Spoon into eight individual serving dishes or goblets. Refrigerate several hours before serving.

Chocolate Mousse

8 servings: each 290 cal., 3 fruit, 1 meat, 3 fat

In a nonstick skillet, combine over medium-low heat

**3 oz. unsweetened baking
chocolate**

6 T margarine or butter

Beat together

6 egg yolks

**1 ½ cups thawed,
unsweetened, pear-
grape concentrate**

**2 T unsweetened orange-
juice concentrate
(optional)**

When chocolate mixture is melted, slowly add the egg-yolk mixture, stirring constantly. Increase heat to medium-high. Continue stirring until thick (about 3 minutes from the time the mixture begins to bubble). Stir in

1 T vanilla extract

Cool to room temperature. When ready, beat until stiff

6 egg whites

½ tsp. cream of tartar

Fold into chocolate mixture.

Pour mousse into eight individual glasses. Chill several hours before serving. Serve with Whipped Cream Topping (page 153) or Chantilly Cream (page 145).

Chocolate Soufflé

8 servings: each 180 cal., 1½ fruit, ½ bread, ½ meat, 1½ fat

Combine over medium heat

2 oz. unsweetened baking chocolate

1 cup thawed, unsweetened pear-grape concentrate

2 tsps. grated orange rind

3 T margarine or butter

When chocolate has melted, remove from heat. Beat a couple of tablespoonfuls of sauce into

4 egg yolks

Beat yolk mixture into the sauce. Cool to room temperature. Preheat oven to 325° F. Beat until stiff

6 egg whites

½ tsp. cream of tartar

Fold into cooled chocolate mixture. Pour into a buttered 1½-quart soufflé dish. Bake for 30–40 minutes at 325° F.

Lemon Mousse

8 servings: each 150 cal., 1½ fruit, ½ meat, 1 fat

Beat in a double boiler over boiling water until thick

4 egg yolks

1 cup unsweetened apple-juice concentrate

¼ cup lemon juice

4 tsps. grated lemon rind

Refrigerate until cold. Beat until stiff

½ cup whipping cream

Fold into lemon mixture. Refrigerate. Beat until stiff

4 egg whites

¼ tsp. cream of tartar

Fold into cream mixture. Spoon into eight sherbet or wine glasses. Refrigerate until ready to serve.

Orange Soufflé

8 servings: each 114 cal., 1½ fruit, ⅔ meat, ⅓ fat

Beat
    6 egg yolks   **5 T unsweetened apple-**
    2 T grated orange peel   **juice concentrate**
    ⅔ cup unsweetened
       orange-juice
       concentrate

Beat until stiff
    6 egg whites   **½ tsp. cream of tartar**

Fold egg whites into orange sauce. Turn into buttered 1½-quart soufflé dish. Bake at 325° F for 30–40 minutes, or until top is brown and soufflé has pulled away from the sides of the baking dish.

Variation: Pineapple Soufflé: Substitute pineapple-juice concentrate for orange-juice concentrate; eliminate grated orange rind; include ½ cup packed, well-drained, unsweetened crushed pineapple.

Raspberry Mousse

10 servings: each 236 cal., 1¼ fruit, ⅔ meat, 2½ fat

Beat in a double boiler over boiling water until thick
    6 egg yolks   **¾ cup unsweetened**
    1 cup raspberry purée   **apple-juice concentrate**
    (straining optional)   **1 T unsweetened orange-**
                      juice concentrate

Stir in
    6 T butter

When butter is blended, remove mixture from heat. Cool to room temperature. Beat until stiff
    6 egg whites   **½ tsp. cream of tartar**

Fold into raspberry sauce. Refrigerate until cold. Beat until stiff
    1 cup whipping cream

Fold whipping cream into raspberry mixture. Spoon into eight individual serving glasses. Refrigerate several hours before serving.

Strawberry Soufflé

6 servings: each 84 cal., 1 fruit, ⅓ meat

Purée
   **½ lb. fresh strawberries
      (straining optional)**
Beat in
   **¼ cup thawed,
      unsweetened apple-juice
      concentrate**

   **2 T thawed, unsweetened   4 egg yolks
      orange-juice   4 drops red food coloring
      concentrate   (optional)**

Preheat oven to 325° F. Butter a 1½-quart soufflé dish. Beat until stiff
   **4 egg whites
   ¼ tsp. cream of tartar**
Fold into strawberry mixture. Pour into soufflé dish. Bake at 325° F for 35–45 minutes.

Variations: Blueberry Soufflé: Substitute blueberries for strawberries; pear-grape concentrate for apple-juice concentrate; eliminate red food coloring.

Raspberry Soufflé: Substitute raspberries for strawberries; pineapple-juice concentrate for orange-juice concentrate.

PASTRIES

Apple Dumplings

Apple Pie

Baklava

Biscuit Dough

Cherry Pie (or Cobbler)

Cinnamon Rolls

Crumb Crust

Dutch Apple Pie

Eclairs and Cream Puffs

Empanadas

Fudge Pie

Lemon Chiffon Pie

Lemon Meringue Pie

Mincemeat Pie

Nut Crust

Pecan Pie

Puff Pastry

Pumpkin Pie

Sour-Cream Raisin Pie

Sweet Pie Crust

Tart Butter Crust

Tart Cream Cheese Crust

Tarts

Turnovers

Whole-Grain Pie Crust

SUGGESTED TECHNIQUES

Rolling out whole-grain pie and cookie dough is more difficult than rolling out white-flour dough because the high-fiber content of whole-grain dough makes it less cohesive. In order to offset this difficulty, I use the following procedure to roll out pie and cookie dough: Place a piece of waxed paper (at least 14 inches long) on counter. Make a ball of the amount of dough you want to roll out; press dough into a circular shape about one-half-inch thick. Place a second piece of waxed paper on top of dough; roll a few times with rolling pin (trying to roll out the dough too far will cause the waxed paper to wrinkle and break). Gently peel up waxed paper from dough; place waxed paper down again on top of dough and turn the waxed paper and dough "sandwich" over. Gently peel up the second piece of waxed paper from the other side of the dough; place the waxed paper down again on top of dough and roll several times. Repeat procedure until dough is rolled out to the shape and thickness desired. Dust dough with flour at intervals as needed to prevent sticking. If dough rolls out unevenly around the edges, simply press it back into the contours desired. For transfer to pie or tart pans, transfer dough while still on waxed paper (but be sure that it is still not stuck to the waxed paper), turn the dough over into the pan and gently peel up the waxed paper, working from the edges in a circle around toward the center. If dough breaks at any time, simply press it back together.

DIABETICS

Cut Fudge, Pecan and Sour-Cream Raisin fruit pies into ten servings, and Apple Dumplings in half in order to keep within limit of two fruit and three to four fat portions at a given meal or sitting. Avoid the Empanadas unless you bake them instead of deep-frying, and avoid the Mincemeat Pie altogether, if possible. Vegetable portions in pastry servings come from the use of soy flour in the pie crusts.

CALORIE WATCHERS

The high caloric content of pie servings is due to the amount of butter or margarine used in making pie crusts. Conventionally flaky pastries do not come cheaply!

GOURMET SERVING SUGGESTIONS

Try using the Sweet Pie Crust for single crust pies. Combine pie servings with a dessert filling, sauce, or syrup of your choice.

Apple Dumplings

4 dumplings with sauce: each 600 cal., 4 fruit, 2½ bread, 6 fat

Prepare and chill
  **Biscuit Dough (see page
    178)**
Core
  4 medium apples
Remove seeds and chop up apple cores. Combine with
  2 cups water   **2 tsps. butter**
  ⅓ cup unsweetened   **½ tsp. cinnamon**
    apple-juice concentrate

Boil for 5 minutes. Purée in blender. Reserve. Combine
  2 T whole-wheat flour   **¼ cup chopped dates**
  3 T softened margarine   **½ tsp. cinnamon**
  ¼ cup currants or   **¼ tsp. cloves**
    chopped raisins

Preheat oven to 450° F. Fill apple centers with the raisin-date mixture. Roll out dough to ¼-inch thickness. Cut squares large enough to enclose each apple. Brush each square with a little partly beaten
  Egg white

(This keeps dough from becoming soggy.) Brush edges with a little water after placing apple in the center of the square. Bring up the four corners to a point and press edges of dough together. Prick top several times. Place in a buttered 8 × 8-inch pan. Pour puréed sauce over dumplings. Bake for 10 minutes in 450° oven. Reduce heat to 350° F. Baste at that time. Continue baking for 45 minutes, basting at 15-minute intervals. If too much water is lost from the sauce, add a little boiling water to replace the loss.

Apple Pie

8 servings: each 360 cal., 3 fruit, 1⅓ bread, 1 veg, 3½ fat

Prepare a pricked, unbaked pie shell made from a recipe of
  **Whole-Grain Pie Crust
    (see page 189)**
Preheat oven to 450° F.

Combine

5 cups thinly sliced apples (peeling optional)	**½ cup chopped dates**
2 T quick-cooking tapioca	**1 tsp. cinnamon**
½ cup unsweetened apple-juice concentrate	**⅛ tsp. nutmeg**

Stir apples gently until coated. Dot with pieces of
1 T butter
Cover with a pricked upper crust. Dust top lightly with
1 tsp. cinnamon
Bake in 450° oven for 10 minutes.
Reduce heat to 350° F. Bake 35–40 minutes.

Baklava

16 servings: each 225 cal., 2 fruit, ⅓ bread, ⅓ meat, 2½ fat

(Many tasters prefer this to conventional baklava because it is not cloyingly sweet. This is the only recipe in this cookbook that uses white flour, since phyllo, as far as I know, is only available made from white flour.) Leave out at room temperature, tightly wrapped, for about 2 hours prior to use
½ lb. phyllo*
When ready to bake, melt over very low heat
½ cup butter
Chop coarsely
⅓ cup blanched almonds (i.e., without skins)
Finely grind another
⅔ cup walnuts
Stir nuts together with

1 tsp. cinnamon   **¼ tsp. cloves**

Place 10 sheets of phyllo in an 8 × 8 × 2-inch cake pan, buttering each sheet before adding the next one. A feathered pastry brush works best; alternatively, use a paper towel tightly tied at one end to form a handle, with the other end feathered out like a tissue flower. Sprinkle about ¼ cup of nut mixture across the tenth layer. Add 2 more buttered sheets of phyllo, then more nuts, then 2 more buttered phyllo sheets, repeating until nut

*"Phyllo" is an extremely thin strudel dough used in making Greek pastries. It can often be found in the frozen foods section of large supermarkets, and at Greek restaurants and delicatessens and bakeries.

mixture is used up. Finish on top with 10 sheets of phyllo as per bottom, being sure to butter the top layer especially thoroughly. Bake at 325° F. for 1 hour. While baklava is baking, bring to a boil

1⅓ cups unsweetened apple-juice concentrate	1 stick cinnamon
2 T cornstarch	1 whole clove
¼ cup thawed, unsweetened pineapple-juice concentrate	¼ tsp. grated lemon rind

Reduce heat to medium. Let syrup boil gently for 7 minutes. Stir in

1 T vanilla extract   **1 tsp. almond extract**

Turn burner under syrup to the very lowest heat, keeping syrup warm until pastry has finished baking. When pastry is done, top will be golden brown and flaky (it browns in about the last 5–10 minutes of baking). Remove from oven. Cut into four quadrants (four equal squares)* while still hot. Pour the hot sauce over the pastry. Return to the oven for 10 minutes at 325° F. Cool to room temperature before serving.

Biscuit Dough

12 biscuits: each 138 cal., ½ bread, ½ milk, 1½ fat

Preheat oven to 450° F.
Combine

1¼ cups whole-wheat flour	¼ tsp. grated orange peel
½ cup soy flour	1 tsp. baking powder
¼ cup date flour	⅛ tsp. salt
½ tsp. baking soda	¼ tsp. cinnamon

Cut in
   ½ cup butter or
      shortening
When the mixture has a fine-crumb consistency, stir in
   ¾ cup buttermilk
Stir vigorously for 30 seconds, until dough is moistened. Turn the dough onto a floured surface. Knead it gently and quickly for another 30 seconds. Roll dough lightly to ½-inch thickness, and cut into circles with cutter dipped in flour. Bake 10–12 minutes at 450° F.

---

*This is done in order to get the syrup to penetrate the baklava more thoroughly.

Cherry Pie (or Cobbler)

8 servings: each 386 cal., 2½ fruit, 1½ bread, 1 veg, 3½ fat

Preheat oven to 450° F.
Combine

**4 cups fresh or frozen
  pitted dark cherries**
**1 T unsweetened orange-
  juice concentrate**

**½ cup unsweetened pear-
  grape concentrate**
**12 medium dates,
  chopped**
2 T quick-cooking tapioca

Line a 9-inch pie pan with dough from recipe for
**Whole-Grain Pie Crust
  (see page 189)**
Pour mixture into dough, being sure to prick the bottom crust.
Dot with pieces of
1 T butter or margarine
Cover pie with a pastry top. Prick with a sharp knife. Flute the
edges. Bake in 450° oven for 10 minutes. Reduce heat to 350° F.
Bake for another 35–40 minutes.

Cobbler Style: Make a recipe of
**Biscuit Dough (see page
  178)**
Pour the fruit mixture into a buttered 1-quart shallow baking
dish. Place biscuit crust on top of fruit, either as separate biscuits or as one uniform crust.

Variations: Blueberry Pie: Substitute blueberries for cherries;
eliminate orange-juice concentrate.

Strawberry Pie: Substitute diced strawberries for cherries; unsweetened apple-juice concentrate for pear-grape concentrate.

Peach Pie: Substitute peaches for cherries; ¼ cup pineapple-
juice concentrate plus ¼ cup apple-juice concentrate for the
other concentrate, and golden raisins for dates.

Cinnamon Rolls

16 rolls: each 168 cal., $\frac{1}{3}$ fruit, 1 bread, 2 fat

Preheat oven to 350° F.
Roll out between two pieces of waxed paper into oval shape, $\frac{1}{4}$ inch thick

**Biscuit Dough (see page
    178)**
Blend
**4 T butter or margarine $\frac{2}{3}$ cup date flour
4 tsps. cinnamon**
Spread mixture evenly across dough with
$\frac{2}{3}$ cup raisins
Leave the edges uncovered. Roll the dough up across the shortest distance. Seal edge with a small amount of
1 beaten egg
Cut into slices $\frac{3}{4}$–1 inch thick. Place tightly against one another on a buttered cookie sheet or pie pan. Bake at 350° F for 25 minutes.

Crumb Crust

8 single-crust servings: each 181 cal., $1\frac{1}{3}$ bread, 2 fat

Melt
7 T butter or margarine
Stir in
**1 cup toasted whole-wheat $\frac{2}{3}$ cup date flour
    bread crumbs**

Press mixture into a 9-inch pie pan or four 3-inch tart pans. Bake for 8–10 minutes at 350° F. Cool before using.

Dutch Apple Pie

8 servings: each 390 cal., 3 fruit, 2 bread, ½ veg, 4 fat

Prepare and prick an unbaked 9-inch pie crust from ½ recipe of
  **Whole-Grain Pie Crust
    (see page 189)**
Preheat oven to 450° F.
Combine
  **5 cups coarsely chopped
    apples (peeling
    optional)
  3 T quick-cooking tapioca
  ½ cup unsweetened
    apple-juice concentrate**

  **2 tsps. cinnamon
  ½ tsp. cloves
  ¼ tsp. allspice
  ½ cup chopped dates**

Turn into pie shell. Dot with pieces of
  1 T butter
Bake at 450° for 10 minutes. While baking, melt
  6 T butter or margarine
Stir in
  1½ cups date flour
At the end of the 10 minutes baking, remove the pie from oven
and spread the date flour mixture over the top. Return to oven.
Reduce heat to 350° F. Bake for 35–40 minutes.

Eclairs and Cream Puffs

Prepare
  Puff Pastry (see page 186)
Prepare a pudding of your choice. For each cup of pudding,
beat until stiff
  ½ cup whipping cream
Fold whipping cream into pudding. Spread filling on both
halves of puffs. Close to serve. For deluxe presentation, frost
or serve with a syrup.

Empanadas (Mexican Deep-Fried Pies)

8 empanadas: each 300 + cal., ¾ fruit, 1 bread, 1 veg, ⅓ meat, 4 + fat*

Prepare a recipe of
**Whole-Grain Pie Crust
(see page 189)**
but do not use any water. Instead, substitute
2 beaten eggs
Chill dough thoroughly. Prepare
**Mincemeat Pie Filling (see
page 184)**
When ready to deep-fry the empanadas, roll out dough to ¼-inch thickness. Cut into squares 4 × 4 inches, or circles 4 inches in diameter. Divide filling equally among the pieces of dough, placing it in the center of each. Fold empanadas over and press closed. Prick several times with a sharp knife. Deep-fry.

Fudge Pie

8 servings: 340 cal., 2½ fruit, ¼ bread, ¾ meat, 4½ fat

Preheat oven to 325° F.
Prepare ½ recipe of the
Nut Crust (see page 185)
Press into a 9-inch pie pan. Boil for 5 minutes, covered

**1 cup chopped dates (24
medium dates)**
**½ cup butter or
margarine**

**⅓ cup unsweetened pear-
grape concentrate**
**2 oz. unsweetened baking
chocolate**

Stir in
2 tsps. vanilla extract
Purée in blender. Beat in
¼ cup whole-wheat flour   **4 egg yolks**
Cool to room temperature. Beat until stiff
4 egg whites
¼ tsp. cream of tartar
Fold beaten egg whites into fudge batter. Fold mixture into the pie pan. Bake at 325° F for 30 minutes.

*Deep-frying will add 200–400 calories and 4–7 fat portions to each empanada; best avoided by diabetics.

Lemon Chiffon Pie

8 servings: each 235 cal., 2 fruit, ½ bread, ¼ meat, ½ veg, 2 fat

Prepare and bake a 9-inch pie shell from ½ recipe of
Whole-Grain Pie Crust
(see page 189)
Combine and set aside
¼ cup lemon juice   1 tsp. gelatin
Beat in a double boiler until thick (about 10 minutes)
4 egg yolks   1¼ cups thawed,
1 T grated lemon peel   unsweetened apple-juice
**   concentrate**
Stir in gelatin mixture and heat until gelatin dissolves. Cool to room temperature. Beat until stiff
4 egg whites   ¼ tsp. cream of tartar
Fold into lemon mixture. Pour into pie shell. Refrigerate until set.

Lemon Meringue Pie

8 servings: each 270 cal., 2 fruit, ½ bread, ½ meat, ½ veg, 2½ fat

Prepare a baked 9-inch pie shell from ½ recipe of
Whole-Grain Pie Crust
(see page 189)
Prepare and set aside a mixture of
4 T grated lemon rind   4 T cornstarch
4 T lemon juice, freshly   ⅓ cup water
** squeezed and strained**
Combine in a double boiler over boiling water
2 T butter or margarine   1 cup unsweetened apple-
⅓ cup water   juice concentrate
Beat
5 egg yolks
Beat a few tablespoons of the hot apple-juice mixture into the egg yolks, then beat the egg yolks into the apple-juice mixture. Continue beating until thick (7–10 minutes). When thick, stir up the prepared cornstarch mixture and beat into the juice mixture. Continue beating until the custard becomes very thick

(2–3 minutes). Pour into the prepared pie shell. Place plastic wrap on surface to prevent glazing. (If a glaze forms on the custard, the meringue will not adhere to it.) Cool to room temperature.

Prepare
Meringue Topping (see
page 149)

Remove plastic wrap and spread the meringue over the pie. Do not leave any peaks, as these will result in uneven baking of the meringue. Bake at 400° F for 8 minutes. When time is up, turn off oven and leave door ajar. Let pie cool in oven for another 30 minutes. This keeps the meringue from falling upon abrupt contact with cooler air. Refrigerate until ready to serve.

Mincemeat Pie*

8 servings: each, 360 cal., 5 fruit, ½ bread, 1 veg, 2 fat

Let marinate in refrigerator overnight

2 T grated orange peel	**⅛ tsp. each nutmeg,**
2 T grated lemon peel	**cinnamon, cloves,**
2 T lemon juice	**ginger**
½ cup unsweetened pear-	**1 cup raisins**
grape concentrate	**1 cup currants**
2 tsps. vanilla extract	**½ cup water**
2 T brandy (optional)	

When marination is complete, combine dried-fruit mixture with

2 peeled, cored, and	**⅓ cup diced cold butter**
grated tart apples	**or margarine**
	1 T quick-cooking tapioca

Preheat oven to 450° F.
Prepare an unbaked
Whole-Grain Pie Crust
(see page 189)

Pour fruit mixture into pie shell. Cover with top crust and prick with sharp knife. Crimp or flute edges. Bake for 10 minutes at 450° F and 45 minutes at 300° F. Cool before serving.

*Best avoided by diabetics.

Nut Crust

8 single crust servings: each 200 cal., ½ bread, ½ meat, 3 fat

Grind in a blender
1 cup walnuts
Combine with
**½ cup toasted whole-
grain bread crumbs**
Stir in
**6 T melted butter or
margarine**
Press into pie pan and chill thoroughly. Or bake for 7–8 minutes at 350° F.

Pecan Pie

8 servings: each 380 cal., 2 fruit, ½ bread, ½ meat, 1½ veg, 5
fat

Line a 9-inch pie pan with an unbaked
**Whole-Grain Pie Crust
(see page 189)**
And fill with
1½ cups chopped pecans
Preheat oven to 300° F.
Heat in a nonstick pan until thick
**1½ cups unsweetened   2 T cornstarch
apple-juice concentrate**

Stir in
1 T vanilla extract
Remove from heat. Cool to lukewarm. Beat in
2 eggs
Bake at 300° F for 1 hour.

Puff Pastry

6 shells: each 128 cal., ½ bread, ½ meat, 1½ fat

Bring to room temperature by placing in a bowl of very warm
tap water
   2 eggs
Combine and set aside
   7 T whole-wheat flour   **¹⁄₁₆ tsp. salt**
   2 T soy flour
Preheat oven to 450° F. Bring to a boil
   ½ cup water   **¼ cup butter or**
                            margarine
Stir in the flour mixture all at once. Stir vigorously for 15 seconds. Remove from heat and cool just enough to touch. (This
takes about 2 minutes with stirring.) Break an egg into the
warm mixture. Beat vigorously until batter is smooth. Repeat
for second egg. Using either a pastry bag, cake decorator, or
spoon, form the desired shapes on a greased cookie sheet:
mounds for cream puffs and 1 × 4-inch bars for eclairs. Bake
for 15 minutes at 450° F, followed by 25 minutes at 325° F.

Pumpkin Pie

8 servings: each 260 cal., 2 fruit, ½ bread, ½ veg, ½ milk, 2½
fat

Line a 9-inch pie pan with an unbaked
   Whole-Grain Pie Crust
   (see page 189)
Preheat oven to 425° F.
Simmer for 15 minutes
   2 cups (1 16-oz can)   **2 T unsweetened**
      pumpkin   **pineapple-juice**
   ¼ cup unsweetened   **concentrate**
      apple-juice concentrate **¾ cup chopped dates (18**
   2 tsps. margarine   **medium dates)**
Purée in blender. Beat in
   2 eggs   **½ tsp. ginger**
   1 cup evaporated milk   **¼ tsp. nutmeg**
   1 tsp. cinnamon   **1 tsp. cloves**
Pour into the prepared crust. Bake for 15 minutes at 425° F, followed by 45 minutes at 350° F.

Sour-Cream Raisin Pie

8 servings: each 420 cal., 3 fruit, ½ bread, ½ veg, ½ milk, 4 fat

Line a 9-inch pie pan with an unbaked
   Whole-Grain Pie Crust
      (see page 189)
Preheat oven to 425° F.
Beat

3 eggs	**2 tsps. vanilla extract**
1½ cups sour cream	**¼ tsp. grated lemon rind**
¼ tsp. nutmeg	**1 cup unsweetened apple-**
½ tsp. lemon juice	**juice concentrate**

Stir in
   1½ cups raisins
Turn into the prepared crust.
Sprinkle lightly with
   ½ tsp. cinnamon
Bake at 375° F until set (40–45 minutes).

Alternative: Substitute ½ cup yogurt and 1 cup cottage cheese for the sour cream; purée before combining with the apple juice.

Sweet Pie Crust

8 single-crust servings: each 150 cal., ¼ fruit, ½ bread, 1 veg, 2 fat

Blend

½ cup date flour	**3 T butter or margarine**
3 T soy flour	**3 T vegetable shortening**
⅔ cup whole-wheat flour	**1/16 tsp. salt**

Add
   3–6 T ice water
kneading until the dough forms a cohesive ball. Roll out between two pieces of waxed paper. If a prebaked crust is required, bake at 350° F for 20 minutes, or until brown.

Tart Butter Crust

4 shells: each 315 cal., 1 bread, ⅓ milk, 1 veg, 4 fat

Grind in blender
¾ cup whole-wheat flour   6 medium dates
¼ cup soy flour   ₁/₁₆ tsp. salt
Blend in
7 T softened butter
Transfer to a bowl. Make a well in the flour mixture. Add a beaten mixture of
1 egg yolk   1 T lemon juice
1 tsp. vanilla extract   ½ tsp. grated lemon rind
Stir until the mixture forms a cohesive ball. Refrigerate at least 30 minutes. Roll dough out between waxed paper in circles 5 inches in diameter and ¼ inch thick. Line tart pan and prick. Weight down with dried beans or pie weights. Bake in 400° F oven 10–20 minutes or until brown. Unmold shells. Cool before filling.

Tart Cream-Cheese Crust

10 shells: each 160 cal., ½ bread, ⅓ veg, ½ meat, 1 fat

Combine
¾ cup whole-wheat flour   ⅛ tsp. salt
¼ cup soy flour   3 T nonfat dry milk
Cut in
½ cup softened margarine   5 oz. soft cream cheese
When well blended, wrap dough in aluminum foil. Refrigerate 12 hours. When ready, divide dough into 10 equal portions. Roll each portion into a ball. Working with one ball at a time (keep the others refrigerated), roll dough to ⅛-inch thickness between two pieces of waxed paper. Form each pastry over inverted muffin tin. Bake at 450° F for 10–12 minutes or until brown.

Tarts

Prepare prebaked tart shells of your choice. Fill with a pudding of your choice and refrigerate. *Or* prepare any fruit pie filling on stovetop by bringing the mixture to a boil, covering it, and reducing heat to a simmer for 20 minutes. Cool to lukewarm before filling tarts and refrigerate. *Or* make combination tarts by first placing some cooked fruit filling of your choice in the tart and topping it with a pudding of your choice.

Turnovers

8 turnovers: each 300 cal., 1 fruit, 1 bread, ½ veg, ½ meat, 3½ fat

Prepare the pastry dough as described for Empanadas.
Roll out in 4-inch rounds. Fill each round with some of a mixture of

1 cup chopped dark cherries, blackberries, or blueberries	**½ tsp. almond extract**
	2 tsps. quick-cooking tapioca
⅓ cup dark raisins	

Fold over and flute edges. Bake on ungreased cookie sheet for 10 minutes at 450° F, followed by 35 minutes at 350° F.

Variations: Apple Turnover: Substitute peeled, chopped apple for berries; 2 tsps. cinnamon for almond extract.

Peach Turnover: Substitute thinly sliced peaches for berries; golden raisins for dark raisins.

Strawberry or Raspberry Turnover: Substitute strawberries or raspberries for the other berries; 6 chopped dates for the raisins; eliminate almond extract

Whole-Grain Pie Crust

8 double-crust servings: each 248 cal., 1 bread, 1 veg, 3½ fat

Blend

6 T vegetable shortening	**⅓ cup soy flour**
6 T margarine or butter	**⅛ tsp. salt**
1⅔ cups whole-wheat flour	

Add by tablespoons
4–8 T ice water
After each tablespoon of water added, work dough thoroughly. When dough forms a cohesive ball, stop adding water. Roll out dough between two pieces of waxed paper. If a prebaked crust is required, line pie pan with one-half recipe of this dough and prick. Bake at 350° F for 20–30 minutes or until brown.

PUDDINGS AND CUSTARDS

Apple Bread Pudding
Banana Custard
Banana Pudding
Bread Pudding
Chocolate Custard
Chocolate Pudding
Kugel
Plum Pudding
Orange Custard
Passover Banana Kugel
Rice Pudding
Spiced Coffee Custard
Strawberry Pudding
Vanilla Raisin Custard
Tapioca Pudding

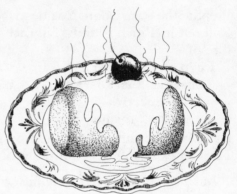

CAUTION

Be sure to prepare puddings in exactly the order given; hot milk is curdled by juice or dried fruit unless the milk is first thickened with cornstarch or arrowroot powder and the juice mixed with egg before adding to the thickened milk.

GOURMET SERVING SUGGESTIONS

Bake a meringue onto a baked pudding or custard; serve as is, or with a main course or dessert syrup of your choice. Serve puddings with filling or sauce of your choice, garnished with Whipped Cream Topping.

Apple Bread Pudding

12 servings: each 240 cal., 3 fruit, 1½ bread, 1 fat

Core and dice (peeling optional) enough apples to make
   7 cups diced apples
Mix with
   1½ cups chopped dates   2 tsps. cinnamon
   (36 medium dates)   ¼ tsp. cloves
Remove the crust from each slice of
   **1 loaf (1 lb.) whole-wheat
   bread**
Butter each slice. Use about ¾ tsp. butter or margarine per slice; this will equal a total of
   **¼ cup butter or
   margarine**
Butter a 2-quart-deep baking dish. Line with about one-third of the bread. Spread with half of the apple mixture, then add another layer of bread; then spread the remaining apple mixture, then the remaining bread. Pour over the casserole
   **½ cup thawed,
   unsweetened apple-juice
   concentrate**
Bake at 350° F for 20 minutes. Press top layer with a spatula at that time in order to compress the pudding. Bake another 20 minutes.

   Alternative: Add ¼ cup dark rum along with the apple-juice concentrate.

Banana Custard

8 servings: each 120 cal., 1½ fruit, ½ milk, ⅓ meat

Purée, adding ingredients in the following order
   3 eggs   ½ cup thawed,
   2 cups mashed banana   unsweetened apple-juice
   ¾ cup nonfat dry milk   concentrate
                 1 cup water
Pour mixture into oiled 1½-quart baking dish or 8 custard cups. Bake at 350° F until set, about 30 minutes.

Banana Pudding

8 servings: each 100 cal., 1 fruit, ⅓ milk, ½ meat

Purée and set aside

3 eggs
1 cup mashed banana

¼ cup thawed,
unsweetened apple-juice
concentrate

Beat together

1¼ cups milk
4 T cornstarch or
arrowroot powder

5 T noninstant milk
powder

Pour into top of double boiler over boiling water, and beat with a whisk or electric beater until thickened. Beat a couple of tablespoons of the milk mixture into the egg mixture, then beat the egg mixture into the milk mixture. Continue beating for 10–15 minutes until thick. Chill.

Bread Pudding

12 servings: each 136 cal., 1 fruit, ½ bread, ⅓ milk, 1 fat

Combine, and set aside

¼ cup raisins

2 T water

In a bowl, combine

1 cup diced, whole-wheat
bread

½ cup date flour

Beat together

1¼ cups milk
3 T nonfat dry milk

1 egg
2 tsps. vanilla extract

Pour liquid evenly over the bread mixture, tossing with a fork in order to distribute the moisture uniformly. Stir in the raisins with their water. Turn mixture into a well-buttered 8-inch square baking dish. Bake at 350° F for 45 minutes or until pudding is set. Pour on

Hot Buttered Rum Sauce
(see page 149)

Let stand several minutes before serving (or keep warm in oven).

Chocolate Custard

6 servings: each 130 cal., 1 fruit, ½ milk, ½ meat, ½ fat

Bring to a boil in a nonstick pan

½ cup thawed,   **1 tsp. butter**
    unsweetened pear-grape
    concentrate

Stir in

3 T unsweetened cocoa
    powder

When cocoa is dissolved, stir in

1 tsp. vanilla extract

Remove from heat. Cool to room temperature. Beat together with

3 eggs   **3 T nonfat dry milk**
1½ cups milk

Pour into oiled 1-quart baking dish or 6 oiled custard cups. Bake at 350° F until set (about 30 minutes).

Chocolate Pudding

6 servings: each 140 cal., 1 fruit, ¾ milk, 1 fat

Beat together and set aside

2 eggs   **½ cup thawed,**
1 tsp. vanilla extract   **unsweetened pear-grape**
1 tsp. thawed,   **concentrate**
    unsweetened orange-
    juice concentrate

Beat together and set aside

1½ cups milk   **2 T nonfat dry milk**
3 T cornstarch

Melt in top of double boiler over boiling water

1 oz. unsweetened baking   **1 tsp. butter or margarine**
    chocolate

When baking chocolate is melted, stir in the milk mixture. Stir continually until thick, then remove from burner. Beat some of milk-chocolate mixture into egg mixture. Return milk mixture to burner over boiling water, and beat in the egg mixture. Beat with whisk or electric mixer for about 10 minutes. Chill.

Kugel (Jewish Noodle Pudding)

16 servings: each 184 cal., 1½ fruit, 1 bread, 1 meat, ½ fat

Soak for 24 hours in refrigerator, stirring once after 12 hours
2 cups raisins   **2 cups milk**

When ready to cook, remove raisins and milk from refrigerator and set aside. Bring to a boil
3 quarts water   **2 T oil**

Add
**4 cups (8 oz.) flat whole-
 wheat noodles**

Cook until tender, about 10–15 minutes. Purée
½ cup sour cream   **4 eggs**
½ cup cottage cheese

Pour off milk from raisins and beat milk into egg-cheese mixture along with
**¼ cup thawed,
 unsweetened pineapple-
 juice concentrate**

**¼ cup thawed,
 unsweetened apple-juice
 concentrate**
¼ cup nonfat dry milk

When noodles are cooked, drain and stir in
2 T butter or margarine

Butter a 2-quart baking dish. Stir liquid and raisins into noodles. Turn mixture into the baking dish. Bake at 325° F for 45 minutes.

Lower-Fat Alternative: Substitute yogurt for sour cream.

Plum Pudding

10 servings: each 210 cal., 2 fruit, ⅔ bread, ⅓ meat, 1 fat

Toss together
⅔ cup date flour
**¾ cup toasted whole-
 wheat bread crumbs**
¾ cup dark raisins
¾ cup currants

**⅓ cup very cold
 margarine, cut into
 small bits**
1 tsp. cinnamon
½ tsp. nutmeg
Pinch of mace

Beat together, and stir into fruit-flour mixture

2 egg yolks	**1 T thawed, unsweetened**
1 T thawed, unsweetened	**orange-juice**
pear-grape concentrate	**concentrate**
1 T grated lemon rind	**4 T grated orange rind**

Beat until foamy
    2 egg whites
Add
    ¼ tsp. salt
Beat until stiff and fold into the batter. Pour batter into a well-buttered 1-quart mold and steam for 1½–2 hours. Serve hot with warm Cherry Sauce.

Alternative: Add 1 T Cognac.

Orange Custard

6 servings: each 150 cal., 2 fruit, ½ milk, ⅓ meat

Beat together

2 eggs	**⅓ cup thawed,**
1¼ cups buttermilk	**unsweetened apple-juice**
⅔ cup thawed,	**concentrate**
unsweetened orange-	**3 T nonfat dry milk**
juice concentrate	

Pour into 6 oiled custard cups or 1-quart baking dish. Bake at 350° F until set.

Variation: Pineapple Custard: Substitute pineapple-juice concentrate for orange-juice concentrate.

Passover Banana Kugel

10 servings: each 172 cal., 1 fruit, 1 bread, ½ meat

Crumble enough whole-wheat matzoth to make
    3 cups whole-wheat farfel*
Pour boiling water over farfel. Drain within 20 seconds so that farfel is moist but not soggy. Beat together

4 eggs	**⅓ cup thawed,**
¾ cup water	**unsweetened apple-juice**
2 medium bananas,	**concentrate**
mashed	

*Farfel is coarsely crumbled matzoth.

Stir into farfel along with
½ cup chopped walnuts
Turn farfel mixture into an oiled 1½-quart baking dish. Bake at
325° F for 45 minutes.

Variation: Apple Kugel: Substitute 1½ cups grated apple for
banana and add 2 tsps. cinnamon.

Rice Pudding

16 servings: each 117 cal., 1 fruit, 1 bread, ⅓ meat

Soak for 24 hours, stirring once at 12 hours
1 cup raisins   **3 cups milk**
When ready to cook, remove raisins and milk from refrigerator
and set aside. Bring to a boil
1¾ cups water   **2 tsps. cinnamon**
⅔ cup brown rice   **¼ tsp. nutmeg**
Cover. Reduce heat to medium-low and simmer for 30 minutes. Turn off heat and let stand on the burner, still covered.
Beat raisin-milk mixture with
3 eggs   **concentrate**
¾ cup thawed,   **⅓ cup nonfat dry milk**
  unsweetened apple-juice
Stir the rice to cool it. Mix liquid and rice together and turn
into an oiled 2-quart baking dish. Bake at 350° F for 30–40 minutes. Serve chilled.

Alternative: Substitute ¼ cup rum and ½ cup sour cream for
corresponding amount of milk in soaking raisins.

Spiced Coffee Custard

6 servings: each 125 cal., 1 fruit, ½ milk, ½ meat

Combine
½ tsp. cinnamon   **2 T boiling water**
1 tsp. instant
  decaffeinated coffee

When coffee is dissolved, stir in
   2 T thawed, unsweetened
      orange-juice
      concentrate
Beat in
   3 eggs   **3 T nonfat dry milk**
   1½ cups milk   **6 T thawed, unsweetened**
                                    pear-grape concentrate
Pour into oiled 1-quart baking dish or 6 oiled custard cups.
Place in a 350° F oven, and bake 30–40 minutes.

Strawberry Pudding

6 servings: each 114 cal., 1 fruit, 1 milk

Purée enough strawberries to make
   1 cup strawberry purée
      (straining optional)
Beat into the purée and set aside
   6 egg whites   **1 T thawed, unsweetened**
   ½ cup thawed,   **orange-juice**
      unsweetened apple-juice **concentrate**
      concentrate

Beat together
   1 cup milk   **4 T nonfat dry milk**
   5 T cornstarch or
      arrowroot powder
Pour milk mixture into top of double boiler over boiling water.
Stir until thick, scraping the pot regularly as the thickening liquid begins to coat the sides. Remove from heat and beat a couple of tablespoonfuls into the egg mixture. Return milk
mixture to heat and gradually beat in the egg mixture. Continue beating about 10 minutes, until eggs are cooked. Stir in

   ¼ tsp. almond extract
Remove from heat. Chill.
   Variations: Raspberry Pudding: Substitute raspberries for strawberries; pineapple-juice concentrate for orange-juice concentrate.
   Pineapple Pudding: Substitute canned, unsweetened crushed
pineapple for strawberries; pineapple-juice concentrate for apple-juice concentrate, and apple-juice concentrate for orange-
juice concentrate.

Vanilla Raisin Custard

6 servings: each 200 cal., 2 fruit, ½ milk, ½ meat

Soak for 24 hours, stirring once at 12 hours
¾ cup raisins   **2¼ cups milk**

When ready to cook, beat in
3 eggs   **2 tsps. vanilla extract**
¼ cup thawed,   **3 T nonfat dry milk**
unsweetened apple-juice
concentrate

Pour into 6 oiled custard cups or a 1-quart oiled baking dish. Bake at 350° F until set.

Tapioca Pudding

6 servings: each 126 cal., 1½ fruit, ½ milk, ½ meat

Beat together
2 cups milk   **3 T quick-cooking tapioca**
4 T nonfat dry milk

Pour into double boiler over boiling water, and cook for 10 minutes, stirring occasionally. At the end of 10 minutes, beat a couple of tablespoons of the milk mixture in with

½ cup thawed,   **2 eggs**
unsweetened apple-juice
concentrate

Beat the egg mixture slowly into the tapioca mixture. Cook for another 10 minutes, stirring frequently. Remove from heat, and stir in
2 tsps. vanilla extract
Chill.

5

Unsweetened Snacks

Crackers
Miscellaneous Mixables
Spreads

Adult Americans, on the average, consume two to three times as much protein as they need. This section is offered in order to give some examples of foods that lend themselves to balanced but moderate protein in combination with complex carbohydrates. There are two basic methods for obtaining complete protein using complex carbohydrate sources. One is by combining complementary vegetable sources. The other is by using small amounts of animal protein in order to complement the vegetable protein. Examples of the former are Mexican corn tortillas with beans, Middle Eastern pita bread with chickpeas and sesame seeds, American bread with peanut butter, Oriental rice with soy-bean curd (tofu), and East European barley-potato-pea soups. Examples of the latter are traditional Mexican chili (a lot of pinto beans with very little meat); traditional Oriental dishes in which very small amounts of egg, meat, or fish are prepared in combination with relatively large portions of rice; Italian pastas served with meat or cheese and milk sauces; and Indian chapatis with cucumber-yogurt spread (raita).

DIABETICS

If you decide to splurge on a relatively high fat (3–4 fat portions) dessert, you can round out the meal with no sacrifice of protein if you drink a glass of skim milk or have a serving of plain nonfat yogurt along with a nutritious lowfat complex carbohydrate food (e.g., nonfried rice, Kasha, Refried Beans, whole grain noodles with tomato sauce, etc.)*

*In nature, proteins are invariably associated to a greater or lesser degree with fat.

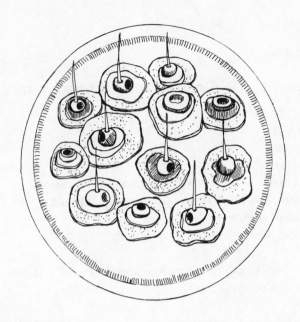

CRACKERS

Bran Crackers
Corn Crisps
Potato Halves
Rice Snaps
Rye Crisps
Seven-Grain Crackers
Whole-Wheat Crackers

The main advantage of these crackers is that they are totally salt free, yet also very flavorful. A variety of grains are used in order to offer a wider source of complex carbohydrates than one ordinarily gets in commercially made crackers. In making crackers, nonstick cookie sheets are a worthwhile investment.

SUGGESTED METHOD

Form dough into logs about 1 inch in diameter on square pieces of waxed paper. The dough may be chilled or frozen at this time by folding the waxed paper over the log and enclosing it in plastic wrap. To make crackers, cut off pieces about ¼ inch thick. Press each slice flat to about ⅛-inch thickness on greased cookie sheet.

Bran Crackers

4 dozen: each 14 cal., 6 crackers equal ½ bread, ⅙ milk, ⅙ meat, ⅔ fat

Bring to a boil
  ½ cup water
Stir in a mixture of
  ½ cup bran   **2 tsps. tarragon**
  ½ cup whole-wheat flour   **¼ tsp. cloves**
  ¼ cup nonfat dry milk
Remove from heat. Beat in
  1 egg
Form into two logs. Slice into rounds. Press flat on cookie sheets, each oiled with
  1 T oil
Bake at 350° F for 12 minutes.

Corn Crisps

4 dozen: each 19 cal., 6 crackers equal 1 bread, ½ meat, ½ fat

Bring to a boil
  1 cup water
Vigorously stir in a mixture of
  1 cup cornmeal   **½ tsp. garlic powder**
  ¼ cup nonfat dry milk   **⅟₁₆ tsp. black pepper**
  2 tsps. basil
Remove from heat. Beat in
  1 egg
Form into logs on waxed paper. Slice evenly and press slices into 2-inch rounds, each about ⅛ inch thick, on cookie sheet greased with
  1 T oil
Bake at 350° F for 12 minutes.

Potato Halves

12 halves: each 85 cal., 1 bread, ¼ fat

Wash and slice in half lengthwise
  6 potatoes

Place cut side down on a cookie sheet oiled with
1 T oil
Bake at 350° F for 30 minutes. Turn oven off. Let potatoes remain in oven for another 30 minutes. Refrigerate. Serve with 2 T cottage cheese, ½ T Enriched Peanut Butter, or thin slices of hard cheese.

Rice Snaps

4 dozen: each 20 cal., 6 crackers contain 1 bread, ½ meat, ½ fat

Bring to a boil
1 cup water
Stir in mixture of

1 cup brown rice flour　　**⅙ tsp. black pepper**
¼ cup nonfat dry milk　　**¹⁄₁₆ tsp. Chinese 5-spice or**
3 T toasted sesame seeds　　**ground coriander**
½ tsp. onion powder

Remove from heat. Beat in
1 egg
Form into logs on waxed paper. Slice and pat out into 2-inch rounds, ⅛ inch thick, on cookie sheets, each greased with
1 T oil (3 T oil total)
Bake at 350° F for 20 minutes.

Rye Crisps

4 dozen: each 12 cal., 6 crackers contain ⅔ bread, ½ meat, ⅔ fat

Bring to a boil
¾ cup water
Vigorously stir in

¾ cup rye flour　　**½ tsp. dill weed**
¼ cup soy powder　　**¼ tsp. garlic powder**
2 tsps. caraway seeds

Remove from heat. Beat in
1 egg
Form into two logs on waxed paper. Slice into pieces, pressing each piece out in 2-inch rounds, ⅛ inch thick, on nonstick cookie sheets, each greased with
1 T oil
Bake at 350° F 12–15 minutes.

Seven-Grain Crackers

8 dozen: each 12 cal., 6 crackers contain $\frac{2}{3}$ bread, $\frac{1}{2}$ meat, $\frac{1}{3}$ fat

Heat to steaming, stirring frequently with a wooden spoon

1 cup Creamed Cereal (see
    page 206)
3 tsps. tarragon

$\frac{1}{4}$ tsp. cloves
$\frac{1}{4}$ tsp. nutmeg
1 T margarine

Stir in

$\frac{1}{2}$ cup whole-wheat flour
$\frac{1}{2}$ cup rye flour

$\frac{1}{4}$ cup soy flour

Remove from heat. Beat in

2 eggs

Form into four logs on separate pieces of waxed paper. Slice. Press flat in four batches on cookie sheets, each greased with

1 tsp. oil

Bake for 40 minutes at 350° F.

Whole-Wheat Crackers

5 dozen: each 17 cal., each 6 crackers equals $\frac{2}{3}$ bread, $\frac{1}{2}$ meat, $\frac{3}{4}$ fat

Blend

$\frac{3}{4}$ cup whole-wheat flour
2 T soy powder

1 tsp. almond extract

Stir into a boiling mixture of

$\frac{3}{4}$ cup water
4 T peanut butter

$\frac{1}{2}$ tsp. nutmeg

Remove from heat. Beat in

1 egg

When dough is lukewarm, pack into two logs on separate pieces of waxed paper. Slice. Pat into 2-inch rounds, $\frac{1}{8}$ inch thick, on cookie sheets, each greased with

1 T oil

Bake at 350° F for 12–15 minutes.

MISCELLANEOUS MIXABLES

Corn Pudding
Cottage Cheese Sauces
Creamed Cereal
Granola
Indian Fried Rice
Kasha
Roasted Nuts and Seeds
Vegetable Medly
Yogurt

Please note that although we are accustomed to eating such items as beans, rice, cooked vegetables, and sauces hot, they are also good as snacks either cold or at room temperature.

Corn Pudding

6 servings: each 120 cal., 1 bread, 1 meat

Beat

2 eggs	**½ tsp. nutmeg**
2 cups milk	**¼ tsp. cloves**

Stir in

½ cup soy grits	**2 cups frozen corn kernels**

Turn into a buttered 1-quart casserole. Bake at 350° F for 35–40 minutes. May be served with rice.

Variation: Substitute peas for corn; 1 tsp. garlic powder for nutmeg; and cracked wheat (bulgur) for soy grits.

Cottage Cheese Sauces

5 servings: each 50 cal., ¼ milk, ½ meat

Mexican: Purée

1 cup cottage cheese	**½ tsp. onion powder**
¾ cup canned tomatoes	**¹⁄₁₆ tsp. red pepper**
½ tsp. cumin	**powder**
½ tsp. garlic powder	**1 tsp. oregano**

If to be served warm, heat gently in double boiler or microwave oven.

Variations: Sweet Herb: Substitute ½ cup milk for the tomatoes; substitute ½ tsp. dried chervil, ¼ tsp. dried chives, ¹⁄₁₆ tsp. cinnamon, and dash of pepper for the spices listed for Mexican sauce.

Italian Tomato: Eliminate cumin and red pepper, add ¼ tsp. sage.

Italian Cream: Substitute ½ cup milk for tomatoes; eliminate cumin, oregano, and red pepper, and add 1 T dried parsley flakes.

Creamed Cereal

10 servings (5 cups): each 163 cal., 1½ bread, ¼ milk, 1 fat

Stir into preheated skillet over medium-high heat

2 T oil
½ cup barley
**½ cup soy flakes or soy
grits and/or cornmeal**

**½ cup brown rice and/or
millet**

Sauté 5 minutes, stirring frequently. When lightly toasted, add

1 cup oats   **5 cups boiling water**

Cover. Reduce heat to medium-low and simmer for 45 minutes. Purée about 2 cups (loosely packed) at a time with ½ cup milk each time for a total per recipe of

2 cups milk

Granola

10 servings: each 300 cal., 2 bread, 1½ meat, 2 fat

Combine in a large bowl

4 cups rolled oats
½ cup wheat germ
¼ cup sesame seeds
¼ cup sunflower seeds

½ cup chopped cashews
**½ cup chopped unsalted
peanuts**

Stir in

2 cups boiling water   **1 T vanilla extract**
2 T oil

Spread evenly on two well-greased cookie sheets. Bake at 350° F for 30–40 minutes until crisp.

Indian Fried Rice

5 servings (4 cups): each 200 cal., 2 bread, ½ veg, 1⅓ fat

Dice

2 bunches scallions   **3 cloves garlic**

Heat a skillet. Add

2 T oil

Turn the chopped vegetables into the pan along with

1 cup brown rice

Sauté for 5 minutes. Stir frequently. Add

2½ cups boiling water   **1 tsp. coriander powder**
½ tsp. curry powder

Cover. Reduce heat to medium-low and simmer for 30 minutes. Stir in

**½ cup frozen corn or
peas**

Cover again and turn off burner. Let stand 15 minutes.

May be served for protein balancing in the following proportions: ¾ cup Fried Rice to 1 T roasted nuts plus 2 tsps. roasted seeds *or* ¼ cup Cottage-Cheese Sauce *or* ½ egg *or* 1 oz. broiled meat or fish.

Variations: Spanish Rice: Substitute 1 tsp. cumin plus 1 tsp. oregano and ⅛ tsp. red pepper for coriander and curry, and substitute 1 cup tomato juice for corresponding amount of water; eliminate corn/peas.

Alternatives: To eliminate fat, omit both vegetables and sautéeing, or eliminate sautéeing and add very finely chopped vegetables twenty minutes into the cooking process, except for garlic, which should be added at the beginning. For grain variety, substitute barley (preferably *not* pearled; see Glossary) for part or all of the rice.

Kasha

5 servings: each 85 cal., 1 bread, ⅓ meat, 1 veg.

Bring to a boil
  ½ cup tomato sauce   ⅓ cup soy flakes or soy
  2½ cups water   grits
  ⅔ cup coarse buckwheat
    groats (kasha)
Cover. Reduce heat to medium. Simmer for 15 minutes.

Roasted Nuts and Seeds

The optimum nuts you can use in terms of maximizing protein per calorie are:
  black walnuts   peanuts (actually a legume)
  Brazil nuts   pine (pignolia) nuts
  cashews   pistachio nuts
The optimum seeds to use are:
  pumpkin seeds
  sesame seeds
  squash seeds
  sunflower seeds
Roast any of these at 300° F for ½ hour or, better, 250° F for 1 hour, 4 cups at a time per cookie sheet. Lower roasting temperature destroys fewer nutrients.

Vegetable Medley

4 servings: each 60 cal., 1 veg, ⅔ fat

Sauté for 5 minutes, stirring frequently

1 T oil   **2 bunches scallions,**
2 cloves garlic, minced   **chopped**

Add

2 green peppers, chopped   **2 tomatoes, chopped**

Cover. Reduce heat and simmer 5–10 minutes. Serve over rice or pasta, topped by Cottage Cheese Sauce or your choice of 1–2 T nuts, 1 oz. meat or cheese or fish, ½ egg, scrambled or hard-cooked and diced.

Variations: 1. Substitute zucchini for green peppers.

2. Substitute mushrooms and/or diced white squash for green peppers, and 2 T water for the tomatoes.

3. *Ratatouille:* Sauté cubed eggplant along with the garlic and onions; add diced celery along with the green peppers and tomatoes, plus 1 tsp. oregano.

4. Substitute any, or combination of, cauliflower, broccoli, carrots, corn, or green peas for green peppers and tomatoes; add 2 T water plus 1 tsp. Worcestershire sauce or 3 T vegetable stock or bouillon.

Yogurt

8 servings (1 quart): each 70 cal., ⅔ milk

Boil

3 cups water

Beat 1 cup of water into

⅔ cup nonfat dry milk

Combine with the remainder of the water. Add

⅔ cup evaporated skim
milk

Cool to lukewarm. Beat in

1 tsp. plain active yogurt
(Dannon is reliable.)

Set in warm (not hot) water. Let stand at 110° F for 4–8 hours. This low temperature can be obtained on an electric stove top by placing a grill between the water container and the burner.

SPREADS

Cottage-Cheese Dips
Enriched Peanut Butter
Hummus
Peanut Butter
Refried Beans

The emphasis in this section is upon providing a relatively high-protein content in proportion to the fat content, as well as in keeping saturated fats relatively low as compared to unsaturated fats.

For particularly low-calorie snacks, I recommend the spreads or dips with vegetables as follows:

1. "Sandwiches" of the spread with lettuce, spinach, Swiss chard, cabbage, etc., instead of the bread;

2. Fresh raw vegetables, such as green peppers, red peppers, green beans, cucumbers, mushrooms, tomatoes, carrots, celery, zucchini, yellow squash;

3. Lightly steamed vegetables, such as cauliflower and broccoli (I do not recommend eating these raw).

Cottage-Cheese Dips

1 cup: 231 cal. (1 T equals 15 cal.), ⅔ milk, 3 meat

Purée

2 T lemon juice
1 cup cottage cheese

1 tsp. Worcestershire
sauce
¼ cup garlic powder

Variations: Dill Dip: Substitute 1 tsp. dill weed for Worcestershire sauce.

Curry Dip: Add 1 tsp. curry powder and ¼ tsp. onion powder.

Chive Dip: Eliminate all but the cottage cheese, and add instead ¼ cup plain yogurt, 1 T apple-cider vinegar, 2 tsps. dried chives, ½ tsp. dried chervil, 1 T dried parsley.

Enriched Peanut Butter

3½ cups: each T 95 cal., ⅓ milk, ⅓ meat, ½ fat

(Like the sugared, hydrogenated commercial peanut butters, this peanut butter is sweet, smooth, and won't separate out even at room temperature; in addition, it offers a balanced protein combination.)

Beat with electric mixer or in food processor

1 lb. nonhydrogenated
peanut butter (2 cups)

2 cups noninstant, nonfat
dry milk
½ cup peanut oil

Hummus (Middle Eastern Chickpea Dip)

16 servings (4 cups): each 90 cal., ½ bread, ⅔ meat, ½ fat

Bring to a boil

3 cups water
1 cup dried chickpeas
(garbanzos)
⅓ cup toasted sesame
seeds
2 tsps. garlic powder

1 tsp. coriander
½ tsp. cinnamon
¼ tsp. turmeric
⅛ tsp. cloves
⅛ tsp. marjoram

Reduce heat to medium-low. Cover and cook 1½ hours. Stir in

½ cup lemon juice

Cover and cook another 30 minutes. Purée with

¼ cup peanut butter

Peanut Butter

1 cup: each T 75 cal., ⅓ veg, ⅓ meat, 1 fat

Purée at top speed in blender until desired consistency is reached

1 cup roasted peanuts   3 T peanut oil

Variations: Sesame Butter: Substitute roasted sesame seeds for peanuts, and sesame oil for peanut oil.

Cashew Butter: Substitute roasted, unsalted cashews for peanuts, and safflower or sunflower oil for peanut oil.

Refried Beans

16 servings (4 cups): each 53 cal., ⅔ bread, ⅔ veg

Bring to a boil

1 cup water   **2 tsps. garlic powder**
2 cups tomato juice   **2 tsps. onion powder**
1 cup pinto beans   **2 tsps. cumin**
2 tsps. oregano leaves (1   **¼ tsp. red pepper**
tsp. powder)

Stir. Cover. Reduce heat to medium-low and cook for 1½ hours. Purée beans with a sautéed mixture of

1 T oil   **1 bunch scallions,**
2 cloves garlic, chopped   **chopped**
                                  1 green pepper, chopped

Spread on Whole-Wheat Flour Tortillas, using ¼–½ cup per tortilla.

Or grill Refried Beans on Whole-Grain Bread or Corn Chips, covered with grated or very thinly sliced Cheddar cheese.

Glossary

Alcohol. Used as a base for extracts. A close relative, chemically speaking, of sugar; like sugar, it consumes B vitamins in the process of metabolism. However, its adequate metabolization in the human system is further limited by the amount of a special enzyme present—alcohol dehydrogenase; the amounts of this enzyme in the human system allow metabolism of only about ¾ teaspoon of rum or brandy, for example, per hour. Beyond this, alcohol causes central-nervous-system tissue damage; taken before bedtime, even one average drink will disrupt normal sleep patterns, although it initially helps induce lethargy due to its sedative effect.

Anise. The fruit of an herb from the parsley family; it has a licorice flavor. Available both as extract and dried seeds.

Arrowroot powder. Used as a thickener; similar in effect to cornstarch. Superior to cornstarch in that it is very pleasantly flavored, does not leave a floury taste, and has slightly more nutrients per calorie than cornstarch.

Baking soda. Used as a leavening agent. Releases gases when activated by acids such as are found in yogurt, buttermilk, fruit juices, vinegar, and cream of tartar. Ideally, it should be entirely neutralized (activated) before reaching the stomach; otherwise, the unneutralized portion will neutralize some stomach acid, thus interfering with digestion and nutrient absorption. See also Baking powder.

Baking powder. A combination of baking soda and, usually, tartaric acid, cornstarch, and aluminum compounds—the composition of commercial double-acting varieties. Not useful in sugar-free baking when juice concentrates are used because the baking soda in it is overactivated by the combined presence of the juices and the tartaric acid. A homemade substitute for baking powder is one part baking soda to two parts arrowroot or cornstarch and two parts cream of tartar; use about 1 teaspoon of baking soda per 2 cups of flour.

Bananas.   An excellent sweetener in sugar-free cooking; requires only 2 tablespoons of juice concentrate to adequately enhance sweetness of 1 cup mashed banana. Good combined with carob powder; sweetest when skin is speckled with black.

Barley.   Sweet and highly digestible; the "pearled" variety is a refined product that has been milled to remove the highly nutritious outer coating of the barley kernel.

Bran.   From the outer layers of grains; rich in minerals, high in B vitamins and fiber. Wheat bran is most commonly available; rice bran is finer and heavier than most wheat bran.

Buckwheat.   A member of the grass family, not a true cereal grain; bitter unless roasted before making into flour.

Butter.   Over 95% saturated fat, 102 calories per tablespoon. Vitamin A content is lower in winter months because cows are eating less green grass. Salted butter has one hundred times the salt content of sweet (unsalted) butter.

Buttermilk.   High in lactobacillus, which aids digestion; lower in calories and saturated fat than yogurt.

Caffeine.   Found in large amounts in coffee, many soft drinks, and, in lesser amounts, in chocolate. A central-nervous-system stimulant that acts as a drug "upper," and can lead to restlessness, nervousness, insomnia, and lowered blood sugar. In sequential use with alcohol or other tranquilizers it can help promote a cycle of drug abuse (caffeine during the day for "upper," and alcohol during the evening for "downer").

Carob.   A plant whose sweet fruit (in the form of bean pods) is roasted and ground to make a powder similar in appearance to cocoa powder, and somewhat similar in taste. Contains no fat, is high in fiber and calcium, and acts as a natural aid to digestion; sweetness of the powder varies according to the adequacy of the roasting process, and blendability according to the fineness of the grind (the finer, the better).

Chocolate.   One of the worst possible food constituents. Contains large amounts of caffeine; contains oxalic acid, which inhibits calcium absorption; difficult to digest and constipating; extremely high in saturated fat, and so bitter that it requires very large amounts of sweetener in order to make it palatable. Also, it is one of the foods to which children most often develop allergies.

Cinnamon. Sweet spice made from the inner bark of evergreen trees.

Citrus rinds. Lemon and orange rind are particularly effective sweetness enhancers. Both the colored part (the "zest") and the white part are high in flavor; the white part contains bio-flavinoids which aid in the metabolism of vitamin C.

Coconut. A relatively sweet fruit, available in unsweetened, dried form primarily in health-food stores; extremely high in saturated fat.

Coriander. A dried fruit of an herb in the parsley family; similar to cinnamon in flavor.

Corn. For best nutrition, cornmeal should be neither "enriched" nor "degerminated." White corn is sweeter than yellow corn. Corn is the largest kernel member of the grain family. For smoother texture in cooking, cornmeal may be scalded or precooked like oatmeal before mixing with remaining ingredients in a recipe.

Cornstarch. Ground from the nutrient-poor endosperm of the corn kernel; used as a thickener.

Dried fruit. Sun-dried fruit is nutritionally preferable to fruit dried with sulfur dioxide. Sun-dried fruit is often dark in comparison to sulfur-dioxide-dried fruit because the latter may also be bleached with other chemicals in order to obtain a glossy appearance. Dried fruit should be stored in airtight jars.

Eggs. Contain saturated fat, but less saturated than milk or meat fat; consumed in moderation (3–4 yolks per week) they are not a health hazard because they also contain lecithin, a B vitamin which aids in the breakdown of cholesterol. For best freshness, store them in refrigerator large ends up. For best leavening effect, use eggs at least one day but no more than one week old, and have them at room temperature before combining with other ingredients.

Egg whites. Contain no saturated fat; may be used as the only leavening agent in cakes (see Passover Coffee Cake, page 135).

Extracts. Several flavors are available commercially in pure (not imitation) form: almond, anise, lemon, orange, peppermint or mint, and vanilla.

Fruit-juice concentrates.   Although juices lack the fiber of the fresh fruit and some of the vitamins, they are still high in nutrient content as compared to sugar, and have helpful acid and enzyme balances. See Table 1 (page 10) for (partial) nutrient analysis.

Ginger.   Made from the dried root of the ginger plant; powdered it is used in both main and dessert dishes.

Grains.   The major grains are wheat, corn, rice, barley, millet, and rye. Optimally, we should eat as varied a grain diet as possible, to maximize trace nutrient variety, and to minimize likelihood of development of allergies to any one grain. Unmilled whole grain may be stored without much nutrient loss for months and years. Commercially, stone-ground flour is preferable because the lower grinding temperature destroys fewer nutrients. Whole-grain flours do not require sifting.

Honey.   A sugar refined by bees from flower nectar; almost as impoverished nutritionally as white sugar (see Table 1, page 10). Human overconsumption of honey has jeopardized some bee populations because keepers sometimes feed them with cheaper white sugar throughout the winter in order to sell more honey, thus making the bees less healthy.

Mace.   A fragrant, highly aromatic spice made from the dried outer covering of the nutmeg seed.

Margarine.   A stew of partially saturated vegetable oils and chemicals. Actually not much superior to butter in terms of fat saturation, although it does not contain any cholesterol; inferior to butter in terms of the degree to which it has been removed from the original food. Proportionally, same calorie and fat content as butter.

Milk.   A highly nutritious food in its raw form, but with some problems related to processing. Needed pasteurization has deleterious effects upon the vitamins C, E, K, riboflavin, and enzyme contents; preservatives destroy lactobacilli; and unnecessary (cosmetic) homogenization may decrease our ability to metabolize the saturated fats without cholesterol build-up.

Milk, evaporated.   More chemically treated than regular milk. Called for in recipes for its contribution to sweetness by virtue of its higher lactose concentration.

Milk, nonfat dry.   Useful not only as a sweetener, but also as a thickener. Noninstant variety is much smoother and finer in texture than the instant.

Molasses. The least impoverished sugar available, in the black-strap form. Used in otherwise sugar-free cooking for its maplelike flavor.

Nutmeg. The hard, aromatic, sphere-shaped seed of an ever-green tree; enhances the taste similarity of carob to chocolate.

Nuts. In combination with seeds and beans, or with grains, can provide complete protein. Also, supplemented by grains and legumes, nuts and seeds provide the best source of fat in the human diet. Roasting increases flavor, sweetness, and digestibility, but destroys some vitamins and enzymes. Where an emphasis upon healthful production is not emphasized, shelled varieties are treated in chemical baths to help dissolve the outer shells in order to get the nuts out unbroken at lowest possible cost; shells of pecans, walnuts, and almonds are often bleached by manufacturers for cosmetic appeal.

Oils. 120 calories per tablespoon. Peanut and olive oils are monounsaturated; all others are polyunsaturated unless heated to very high temperatures as in deep-frying; best if cold-pressed, since heat destroys some nutrients (especially vitamin E). Probably the most healthful of all cooking would eliminate even the use of oils, and use instead very finely ground nuts or seeds as the source of fat in recipes (see Almond Cake, page 129).

Peanuts. Actually legumes (like peas), not nuts; better sources of protein per calorie than true nuts.

Rice. Brown rice has an almost nutty flavor, and is much more flavorful than white rice. One of the easiest of all grains to digest; recommended first grain for infants.

Salt. Unnecessary as an added chemical in our diets. In very small amounts, salt can enhance sweetness, but too much can lead to a slightly sour taste. Adverse effects of salt overload in the human body are changes in the water balance which lead to bloating—possibly exacerbating predispositions to hypertension—and interference with the normal ion balance of the central and peripheral nervous system.

Seeds. Very high in a broad range of vitamins and minerals, some of which are scarcely available from other food groups. In buying sesame seeds, try to obtain the unhulled variety for best nutrition. See Nuts, above.

Soy. Provides higher and more complete protein for humans

than any other bean; available as dried beans, flakes, grits, curd (tofu), and powder or "flour." If not available in health-food section of your supermarket, can be found in virtually any health-food store. Try to purchase soy powder or "flour" which has not been defatted, since the fat lost is unsaturated and therefore beneficial, and since lecithin is also lost in the defatting process.

Sugar.   As used in this book, the term refers to any sugar which has been extracted from its original food source. Hidden in foods under many different names such as corn syrup, corn sweeteners, corn syrup solids, dextrin, dextrose, brown sugar, turbinado, glucose, fructose, lactose (refined from milk products), milk sugar, mannitol, sorbitol. Highly alkaline, therefore causes excess stomach acid to be secreted in order to neutralize the alkalinity; virtually devoid of vitamins and minerals.

Vanilla.   Available in extracts or as the dried bean; avoid the imitation varieties. Very important in sugar-free cooking since the vanilla flavor offsets the fruit flavors of the natural sweeteners to provide a more standard flavor.

Wheat.   The most popular grain in America. Failure to alternate it sufficiently with other complex carbohydrate sources (other grains and beans) may be one salient factor in the frequency of gluten allergies in children. Available as the whole grain (wheat berry), cracked grain (bulgur), and flours. Whole-wheat flour is 400 calories per cup; white flour is 500 calories per cup—the difference is due to the higher fiber content of the whole wheat.

Whipping cream.   High in saturated fat. Read your labels carefully since some manufacturers use sugar ("dextrose").

Yeast.   Extremely widely used in our culture because leavened breads and cakes are the norm; however, yeast has a health disadvantage in that phytic acid of yeast is detrimental to absorption of many essential minerals. Unleavened breads of other cultures (tortillas, matzoth, chapatis) are all superior to yeasted breads in terms of nutrition.

Yogurt.   Contains lactobacilli which decompose milk sugar (lactose) and which produce vitamins B1, B2, and B12.

Index of Recipes